Everything is Perfect

a memoir

Kate Nason

Be grateful for whoever comes,
because each has been sent
as a guide from beyond.
—Rumi

AUTHOR'S NOTE

When, in the wake of my husband's betrayals and the national scandal that engulfed us, my marriage blew up, the story ran everywhere. *The New York Times, The Washington Post, The Los Angeles Times, People, Time, Newsweek*—I collected them all. To these I added articles sent to me by friends as far away as Tokyo, London, and Berlin, all containing pictures of me they'd clipped from their hometown papers. Then I gathered the countless handwritten pleas from reporters clamoring for interviews, and along with notebooks and journals scrawled with my musings, I stuffed everything into a bulging banker's box labeled THE BOMB. A box I banished to the attic.

For years, this event—the entire decade of my thirties—played through my mind like a mythical journey—complete with heroes and villains, trials, tests, and triumphs. I lived with these memories turning them round and round in my mind, in an attempt to make meaning from my trajectory.

Not until my kids were grown, some fifteen years later, did I dig into that box and begin to write this story.

Correction: the story wrote me.

Often at dawn, before my head came off the pillow, a sentence would download fully formed into my brain. Those sentences unleashed a trove of memories, and all those ghosts came out of hiding.

I did not choose this story. I did, however, choose this husband. This was not my first mistake, and it was not without a whisper of intuition. My life had been a series of missteps, some leading to joy, others to heartbreak. I had lessons to learn —trusting my intuition chief among them. I've had many teachers along the way, some like this husband, I chose. Others —his women—arrived unbidden. The places where their lives intersected mine were unavoidable plot points in my journey.

This is a true story told from my memories, journals, and all those press clippings. I have chosen to use pseudonyms for my central characters, and the conversations herein are not likely verbatim due to the passage of time, though they've been recounted just as I have recalled them.

In a world that strives to reduce us to good or bad, black or white, red or blue, victim or vixen, we must be careful not to oversimplify. Our stories are complex—nuanced. It is in this complexity that we find compassion. Each voice, each story, helps us chart our way forward.

There are many sides to every story. This is mine.

PROLOGUE

I 've often thought how lucky I am that my marriages blew up in such spectacular fashion. No slow moldering. No long years of quiet misery. No need to justify my exit.

My first marriage lasted a matter of months, but I'll save that story for later. It's the tale of my second mistake I wish to tell, and it is quite a doozy. My second husband proposed ten times. It was more a campaign than proposal. The important thing—and I'd like some credit—I said NO nine times. I loved him deeply, was wildly in love. And yet I'd made a vow at the end of my first marriage: Never again would I marry. Ever.

But something else—somewhere deep, I knew I could not trust him. My intuition—that still-small voice—that whispered *no* was still so small I hadn't learned to heed it.

So that tenth proposal? I caved.

In January of 1998, just seven years into my second marriage, the press arrived en masse on our doorstep. A barrage of reporters surrounded our home, all shouting for details regarding my husband's longtime affair with a former student, our frequent babysitter, someone I'd considered a friend. A young woman now at the center of a national scandal.

We were advised to give a press conference with hopes the madness would stop.

Most of that night spools through my head in splintered snapshots: the blinding light of camera flash, the thrash of my heart as I stepped out the door, the chatter of my teeth in the January cold, a shaking in my limbs I could not steady.

There on the same porch that had served as a stage for my daughter's one-act plays and sheltered my son's vast Hot Wheels roadways, we faced the crowd. Their booted feet trampling my flowerbeds, microphones on boom-sticks thrust in our faces. And beyond, a forest of white spires piercing the night sky from news vans and satellite trucks clogging our quaint, tree-lined street.

Flanked by my uncle and a lawyer, my husband and I waited while they addressed the crowd. Then my uncle motioned for us to move forward, and there in the strobe of light caught in winter-bare branches, I stood next to the man I'd married for better or worse as he confessed his affair. He confessed his sins, in front of all of America, and admitted his guilt in a way our President could not.

For a tiny moment, I took heart in this, hoped we'd be okay. But underneath that hope was something deeper, hotter: I despised him.

1

HE SANG TO ME

1988 Culver City, California

I met my second husband on the same day I filed to divorce
my first.

I wasn't looking.

It was a bright and breezy day in early fall. Santa Ana
winds had whipped through Los Angeles overnight and chased
all that thick brown haze out to sea. As I'd headed east on I-10
that morning, the palm trees on either side of the Santa Monica
freeway flounced their underskirts in the breeze. Even the
Hollywood sign, most days a filmy smudge on browned
foothills, stood out cocky and optimistic against a sapphire sky
—the City of Angels on auto-focus.

My attempt to match my mood to the day had failed. For
on that impossibly gorgeous morn, I'd done the thing I'd
dreaded most and handed my one-year-old, Molly, over to her
father for the first of their weekend visits. When he arrived,
Molly clung to me, her short legs ringing my waist, arms tight
around my neck. I kissed her head, nosed her hair, and inhaled

her scent, a blend of bananas and baby shampoo. Hank took her in his arms and off they went, her tiny hand reaching for me as he carted her down the drive, tears streaming her cheeks as he loaded her into the car. My eyes welling as they drove off, I said a prayer for her safety. And then determined to make good use of unwanted free time, I headed straight downtown to file for divorce.

The courthouse in downtown Los Angeles was a bustling place on Saturday mornings, thanks to a free legal clinic that served up a smorgasbord of legal services—in my case a budget divorce—a welcome end to a contentious union.

I felt a momentary victory when the clerk stamped my documents, but despite the relief, I left the courthouse pinging with anxiety. The absence of my daughter throbbed like a missing limb. That last year, taking care of Molly had taken care of me. Without my baby and her babyhood needs to shape my hours and days, I feared I'd fly apart.

Desperate for distraction, I visited my old haunts. I drove to West Hollywood, took a booth at Hugo's, and poked at my salad. Then off to Book Soup on Sunset, where I browsed the shelves scanning books for best first sentences. I drove home and power-walked my neighborhood. When nothing worked, I picked up the phone and dialed my friend Lacey, who promised to come over and keep me company.

Lacey was a neat freak, so I rushed from room to room in an attempt to make order. I gathered Molly's toys scattered on the living room floor into the basket next to the wing chair. Found one little pink sock under the coffee table next to her tattered *Goodnight Moon*. Folded one tiny t-shirt from the mountain of unfolded laundry on the dining room table. Shoved the stack of unopened bills on the kitchen counter into the junk drawer. Stared at the dirty dishes in the sink, washed one plate. And then I gave up, put Joni Mitchell on the stereo—loud—and headed back to the kitchen to gather ingredients for a pitcher of sangria.

"Yoo-hoo," Lacey's voice rang out from the front porch. "We brought dinner!"

"We?" My stomach fell, I took a deep breath and unlocked the door.

"I brought a friend. Kate, this is Charlie. Charlie, Kate." Lacey grinned and in she came, friend in tow.

Just like that, he walked through my front door. He looked like a sandy-haired surfer, his jeans, a sexy slouch on his hips, a faded t-shirt skimming his taut chest.

Charlie smiled at me, blue eyes beaming. I half-smiled, turned my back to him, looked to Lacey and mouthed, *What the hell?* Eyes gleaming, she shrugged, and they followed me into the kitchen trailing the scent of garlic and onions.

"Ooh, Devil Juice!" Lacey laughed as she set the bag of Cuban take-out on the kitchen counter. "Watch out, Charlie, Kate's sangria is deadly." Tall and slender, Lacey had a thick curtain of ash-blond shimmer down her back—a living shampoo commercial. We'd met several years back while still enrolled in the Art History department at UCLA. Three years younger than I—and brilliant—she was already at work on her masters while I was finishing my BA.

She'd mentioned her new friend Charlie just last week. "Great guy," she'd said, "really funny and really cute," and something about a girlfriend he'd left behind in New York City. She'd neglected to mention his age—young—really young.

"What's in it?" Charlie's eyes skimmed over the pitcher and fell on me with a smile that made me feel self-conscious and suddenly pretty.

"Brandy, sugar, red wine, O.J." Discombobulated by his attention, I focused on adding paper-thin slices of bright-green Granny Smiths to the pitcher, gave the ruby red potion a stir, and filled two—make that three—glasses with ice and sangria.

"Man!" Charlie gulped. "Better pace myself." I watched his lips stain red as they met the glass, caught myself and quickly looked away, then turned, and the three of us made the short trek from the kitchen to the living room, glasses in hand.

"Nice fireplace," Charlie said, eyeing the woodbin.

The fireplace was the focal point of my barrel-vaulted living room. I'd rented the Spanish-style bungalow in Culver City when I fled our Venice Beach apartment after a break-in. Our house sat nestled in a neighborhood of small cottages, all in neat rows with well-tended gardens. Unlike Venice, with its rampant crime, and rowdy beach goers, Culver City was quiet, felt insulated, and had an air of safety. Though in those days, I doubted I'd ever feel safe again.

"Mind if I light a fire?" Charlie smiled at me and made for the woodbin.

"Sure, have at it." Flustered, I paced the floor.

The sun had set, and the temperature had dropped. I looked to Lacey, who rubbed her hands together in an effort to warm. Back in the dining room, I turned the thermostat to high and trailed into Molly's room. There in her crib was her beloved Mr. Bear—her father had refused to take it that morning. As always, we'd argued and not wanting to upset Molly, I relented. I carried her bear into the living room and held it up for Lacey to see. "He wouldn't take her bear." She acknowledged my complaint with a nod, then dipped her head in Charlie's direction where he was busy laying the fire and smiled.

I watched as Charlie, down on his knees, his back to me, stacked the kindling and the wood into a perfect pyramid. He struck a match with flair, lit the crumpled newsprint, tipped his head, and blew. The flames caught hold. They did their dance. It was a perfect fire.

"You're good at that," I said.

"Honor scout!" He turned to me and flashed that smile. "Spent my childhood camping in the woods in Wisconsin."

"Hey, let's eat." Lacey chimed.

I fished a checkered tablecloth from the pile of laundry on the dining room table and spread it on the living room floor. The three of us ate our supper of garlic chicken, lemony rice, and fried plantains, picnic-style in front of the fire, Joni Mitchell looping on the stereo.

"So? Did you file?" Lacey asked between forkfuls.

"Yep." Aware of Charlie's eyes on me, I explained, "I spent the morning at a free legal clinic, filing for divorce." He nodded as if he knew. Then I turned to Lacey, "I filed for something called a bifurcation. It means I can file for divorce and leave the custody issues until later."

"Well, that's handy," Lacey smiled and took a swig of her sangria.

"Mandatory," I said. That morning when the lawyer suggested a bifurcation as my quickest route to a divorce, I'd snapped it up, knowing that it could take years to reach a custody agreement with Hank given our clashes around parenting.

Lacey raised her glass. "To freedom."

"Freedom? At what price? Lacey, I'm worried about Molly."

"Custody? Molly?" Charlie interjected.

"Oh, didn't I tell you? Molly's her utterly adorable thirteen-month-old. And I say this in a town full of adorable thirteen-month-olds." Lacey, smiled at me. "Molly's fine, Kate. Hank's a jerk, but he loves her in his own way. She'll be fine, I promise."

It was precisely *his way* I was worried about. What father denies his daughter her favorite stuffed animal and security blanket? Or forbids his daughter to call him Daddy, demanding she call him by his first name instead?

I shuddered, shook my head, and reached for the pitcher to pour another round. Lacey covered her glass. "Nope." She stood up and grabbed her jacket. "Paul's waiting for me."

"I'll have another," Charlie drained his glass, and reached for the pitcher.

"What? You're leaving?" I looked to Lacey; she waved me off, jumped to her feet, and grabbed her coat.

"Mind if I stay?" Charlie flashed a smile.

"I'll call you in the morning. Molly's fine. Relax!" Lacey grinned and out she went, an awkward silence in her wake.

What had Lacey said about me? The question worried me into silence. I twisted my napkin through my fingers and jumped to my feet. Busying myself, I gathered our picnic plates from the floor and marched them to the kitchen. *What the hell was Lacey thinking?* I slid the dishes into the sink with a clatter, ran the water, took a deep breath and returned to the living room where Charlie was stoking the fire.

Without missing a beat, he pulled a joint from his t-shirt pocket and held it up for me to see. "You get high?"

The sangria had served to soothe me somewhat, but anxiety over Molly's absence still needled. Weed would finish the job. I nodded yes, he lit the joint and held it to my lips. I took a hit, a deep breath in, chuffed and exhaled. Then I pulled the throw pillows off the couch, and we settled in front of the fire.

"How old are you, anyway?"

"23," he grinned, took another hit, and coughed.

"Geez," I quickly did the math. "You were still in high school when I graduated from college."

The day went from tight to slack and I found myself floating in a conversation that was chatty and unimportant. A story from work, something funny that Molly had done that week, when suddenly—was it the weed, the wine, the weight of the day, the whole entire wreck of me? I came undone and started to cry. Before I had a chance to apologize, Charlie brushed my hair from my eyes and whispered, "It's okay, you can tell me."

Slowly, I started to speak and then I unspooled the whole damn story. The gist of it, anyway—the break-in during my third trimester, the birth of my daughter just three weeks later, and the speedy breakdown of my brief, bad marriage.

Charlie listened attentively. "God, Kate I'm so sorry," his eyes teared up as I spoke. I kept talking until I had no more tears and no more story. And then he pointed to my guitar in the corner of the room.

"Can I play it?" he asked.

"Sure," I said, switching off Joni mid-Blue.

Stoned, exhausted and somewhere akin to mellow, the firelight flickering across Charlie's face, my legs, the walls—I listened as he played, and then he sang. His voice was deep and clear.

Charlie could sing.

And he sang to me.

All night long.

2

HE FIXED THINGS

A few days after Charlie sang to me in front of the fire, he showed up at my door with a red metal toolbox. Like a male Mary Poppins, he reached into his tool chest and set to work. The toaster, the iron, the timing on the dishwasher, even the simple act of replacing a burned-out light bulb seemed a gift. The entire house had fallen into a cold war of disrepair over the course of my break-up with Hank.

Looking back, I am staggered by the speed with which I fell into this courtship. Caught in Charlie's light after so much darkness. Eight years my junior, his youth made me feel young. And more, he distracted me from my new reality, a life turned upside down on that hot July night, thirteen months prior, when that stranger climbed through my bedroom window.

Our days were filled with flirty banter and often spilled into nights, our frequent dinners slipping into drowsy breakfasts.

Before I knew it, six weeks had flown by.

One Saturday, after I'd formally introduced Molly to Charlie, he came equipped with rope and rubber inner tube. "Today

I'm gonna hang that swing!" The bright yellow toddler swing, another casualty of my marital discord, had languished in the corner of the dining room for months. I watched with deep appreciation as Charlie propped a ladder against the Jacaranda out front. He wrapped the lowest sturdy branch of that towering tree with strips of inner tube and hung the swing with care. Molly squealed with glee as he buckled her in for her maiden voyage.

Charlie was attentive. He had an uncanny ability to know what I needed before I did. Yes, he was kind and cute and smart and funny, but he was also nurturing—a caretaker—good with Molly and with me.

———

One day in mid-December, I was in the kitchen chopping vegetables for the pot of minestrone I'd promised for supper. I scooped up the diced white onion and bright green parsley with the blade of my knife and thumbed them into the pot. They hit the hot olive oil with a sizzle, joined the garlic and all three released their heady perfume.

I watched from the kitchen window, winter sun splashing the street out front, as Charlie pulled up in his old Volvo wagon. My heart bucked at the sight of him. He parked the car, got out, and opened the hatch. I watched as he wrestled with a huge rough-hewn plank of wood.

"Wow, something smells good!" he called through the open kitchen window as he lugged his burden up the driveway, across the front porch, and through the front door. "Hey, look what I've got!"

"What's that?" I wiped my hands on my apron, made my way from the kitchen through the dining room and stopped to lean against the wide archway that opened into the living room.

The late-day sun cast light and shadow on the barrel-vaulted ceiling as it threaded through the leafy lacework of the Jacaranda out front.

"The question, Kate, is not what it is now, but what it is going to be." He laid the plank down in front of the fireplace, grinned, and swooped in to plant a deep kiss on my lips. He turned and ruffled Molly's meringue of curls. "Hey, Molly." She sat in her pint-sized rocker watching Dumbo on the VCR with Mr. Bear, her constant companion, cradled in her lap.

"Dumbo again?" Charlie winked at me and headed back out to his car, returning with two wooden corbels, smoothed and shaped. He set them down beside the plank and faced me with a smile. His jeans, torn at the knees, met his Redwing work boots in a jumble. He swept the mop of hair from his eyes and reached into his carryall, grabbed his worn leather tool belt, and slung it on his hips. "This, Kate, is your new mantle!"

The house on La Salle Street in Culver City was a Santa Fe-style jewel box. Graceful arches led from room to room. Spanish tiles flung a fiesta of color across the kitchen and into the bath. The fireplace was kiva style, no mantel. Four weeks before Christmas, I'd mentioned I needed a place to hang Molly's stocking. By the time I ladled the soup into bowls on my big pine table that night, I had one. Perfectly matched to the architecture of my little bungalow, Spanish-style corbels supporting a salvaged wood plank.

"And look." He dug into a pouch on his tool belt and pulled out three cup hooks. I watched as he screwed them soundly into the underside of my new mantle. "There!" he beamed. "Now where are those stockings?"

———

Later that night, I stood at the sink and washed the dishes.

"Dummo, I want Dummo!" Molly called out.

I laughed, hearing the circus calliope chime from the TV in the living room. I snuck a peek, and there they were, Molly and Charlie. The two of them snuggled into my big down sofa, their voices rising in unison. *"Look out for Mr. Stork, that persevering chap, he'll come along and drop a bundle in your lap."*

Molly loved Charlie and Charlie loved Molly. They could play for hours on the living room floor with the old wooden blocks I'd bought at a preschool going-out-of-business sale, all smoothed edges, a fine patina laid down by many decades of toddlers' hands. They'd build cities and towns, skyscrapers, and bridges, and then they'd lay wooden tracks and run the Brio trains through. The two of them in matching blue-and-white-striped conductor's hats that he pulled out of his magic tool chest one day. And while they built their cities and towns, I'd fold tiny t-shirts, mate toddler socks, and sing along with Dumbo. *"Look out for Mr. Stork. He's got you on his list, and when he comes around, it's useless to resist..."*

Truth? I hadn't planned on this—on him—on dating so soon after my breakup with Hank. But in the wake of all that had happened, I slipped into the role of happy homemaker as I would an old robe and slippers, without thought or question. A child of the early sixties, I was raised on Golden Books—those Mommy stories with their idyllic domestic scenes were written on me. I was relieved to play house, cook, and fold the laundry, while "my man" fixed things. Fixed me? Perhaps.

Nonetheless, I was grateful for his presence in our lives, a good man, a normal guy—an honor scout.

3

CHRISTMAS FEST

My annual tree trimming party was set for the Saturday before Christmas. I'd cancelled it last year in the wake of the break-in, but the gathering was something I'd hosted since college, and I was determined to prove to myself that life could return to "normal." My friends—all with careers in the LA art world—would attend. And this year, so would Charlie.

Charlie would have to pass the Ed test.

My best friend, Ed, and I met on our first day at UCLA, in Italian class. I was instantly drawn to him. He was the class clown, had a laugh like Pee Wee Herman's, and a perfect Italian accent. A head of dark curls flopped into his eyes—curls I would later learn came courtesy of a self-administered perm. By the end of the first week in that classroom, we were sitting side by side. Turns out, in addition to loving all things Italian, we were both art history majors.

After we'd graduated and settled into our careers, we shared the minutiae of our lives by phone; like an old married couple, we discussed the details of our days. Ed worked in the conservation department at the Getty Museum, and despite his exceptional talents in art restoration—he could mend anything —his inability to fix the broken guys he fell for was another matter. We shared this knack for choosing the wrong men, and over the years we'd navigated a collective string of bad boyfriends. He was protective and a bit bossy—often acting more like a big brother, the one I'd wished for growing up as the oldest of three girls. Ed had barely tolerated Hank and I was hoping he and Charlie would hit it off.

"When am I going to meet this guy?" Ed asked over the phone.

"How about dinner Thursday?'

When Ed arrived, Charlie was busy repairing my dining room chairs. I introduced them and watched the two of them size each other up. I saw Ed's bemused expression as he took Charlie in. Ed's eyes lit up and a sly smile crossed his lips. He reached in to shake Charlie's hand, but Charlie held his fingers up, sticky with glue, and returned Ed's smile with one of his own.

Ed and I headed into the kitchen.

"Good God. Adonis in a tool belt." Ed whispered.

"Pretty cute, huh?"

We watched from the kitchen while Charlie, intent on his task, glued the loose rungs of my antique chairs and clamped them to dry, all six overturned on the wide planks of my big pine table. Typically, this would have been Ed's job, but tonight we were on dinner duty. Ed had arrived with his homemade gnocchi. He set a pot of water on the stove to boil, then stood in the doorway and kept a close eye on Charlie's clamping technique while I whipped up a batch of fresh pesto.

"All done!" Charlie came into the kitchen, stood at the sink, turned on the tap with his elbow and rinsed the glue from his fingers. Then he reached for Ed's hand and shook it heartily. "We'll have to eat in the living room tonight, that glue needs to set and dry."

On the way to the living room, Ed stopped to inspect Charlie's workmanship.

Charlie grinned at him. "How'd I do?"

"Nice work." Ed handed Charlie his dish and we carried our dinner into the living room, settling down cross-legged in front of the fire, a fog of garlic levitating from the bowls in our laps.

Over the course of dinner, I sat back and watched the two of them. They had a natural ease with each other, their banter was immediate. I had no idea where my relationship with Charlie was going, but Ed's opinion was important to me. During dinner, they entertained each other. Ed with a story about his job at the Getty and Charlie with something from his work for the artist DeWain Valentine—explaining the job was only temporary, then detailing his plans to land a job in film or theater.

"Hey, Ed," I interjected, "we're going to the Rose Bowl Flea Market on Sunday. I'm looking for a new bed for Molly. Wanna come?" I'd told Charlie that Ed and I often spent weekends combing flea markets and antique shows and I was worried Ed might feel upstaged.

"Wouldn't miss it." Ed grinned, brushing his now-straight hair out of his eyes.

That Sunday the three of us combed the antique-strewn acres of the Rose Bowl, trailing the makeshift pedestrian alleys through a hodgepodge of old lamps, tables, paintings, and house parts. Before long, I found an old spindled headboard, footboard, and side rails. "Hey, what about this one?" I asked, looking at them both to see what they thought. "No slats, though," I added.

"I'll cut some!" Ed volunteered.

"I'll paint it white," Charlie chimed.

They bonded on that day.

Charlie had passed the Ed test.

———

The night before my Christmas party, Charlie, Molly, and I trekked down the street through the neighborhood to pick out a Christmas tree. All three of us were bundled up against a chilly December evening. Molly rode on Charlie's shoulders, her blond ringlets capped with a knit hat, the oversized pompom bobbing in time to her rendition of Jingle Bells.

The next morning, the noble fir Molly had chosen with a pudgy point of her finger as she darted through the makeshift pine forest at the corner tree-lot, stood, fragrant and tall, in the arch of our picture window. Charlie erected the tree in the old red-and-green metal tree stand, adjusting the rusty eye screws, testing for plumb like an exacting carpenter.

"There," he said. "Now for the lights." Charlie strung the tree, top to bottom, with twinkly white lights and Molly did a nonstop jiggly dance as she practiced her patience. Then we decorated the tree, from the treasure chest of my collected vintage ornaments. When our work was done, we paraded out into the front yard and stood beneath the now-leafless Jacaranda to admire our handiwork through the window.

"Mommy, it's magic!" Molly waved her invisible wand through the air and hugged my leg. I hiked her up to my hip.

"Time to get ready to go, Molly. Your dad will be here soon."

"Noooo!" Molly squealed.

I wanted to squeal, too. Things with Hank had grown more contentious. We were polar opposites in the parenting department. We fought over everything—even basics like diet or dress. Once she'd left the house in her favorite pink frills and came home in black, toddler-sized bike shorts, patterned with white skulls and crossbones. Her beloved teddy bear and blanket were still a flashpoint of contention. Months ago, in desperation, I'd dragged Hank to Molly's pediatrician. "Basic babyhood needs," the doctor had explained the importance of transitional objects. Hank rejected this concept categorically. We'd been assigned a court-appointed mediator to help us work out our differences, and though we still had no formal custody agreement, he did have Molly every other weekend. And I dreaded every one.

Hank's newly acquired 1960s Jaguar sedan, complete with right-side steering wheel, sputtered up to the curb out front. I watched from the dining room window as he sauntered up the drive. Years ago, I'd read that swagger as self-confidence, but now I knew it for what it was, a screen for his insecurity, along with his bitter bluster and constant criticism. My stomach rolled at the sight of him, lurched at his forceful pound on the door, I took a deep breath and opened it to let him in. That old familiar aftershave, mixed with sweat, a cloud that hung between us. He was unshaven, and the scruff of tight curls that circled his balding head was a little longer and messier than usual. His steely glare tracked from the Christmas tree and landed with a grimace on the three stockings that hung from my new mantel. "Nice," he hissed.

Hank had always been a Christmas begrudger. His yearly refrain of "no tree this year," would start at Thanksgiving. "Waste of money, such a sham, bad for the planet." We'd argue often and loudly all through December, and then he'd bring one home like a repentant Scrooge. "Surprise! I know it's important to you," he'd say, expecting a reward and a show of gratitude. "Definite control issues," my therapist had said. *No kidding.*

Charlie, half a head taller than Hank, stood behind me in the open doorway. They gave each other a cool nod. Hank lifted Molly from my hip to his. She wriggled in his arms and reached for Mr. Bear.

"Bear?" she said to her father.

"That's right, honey," he hugged Molly and flashed a disgruntled glare at me. I'd recently won this battle in mediation. I handed Mr. Bear to Hank and added her blanket to the mix.

"Have her back on time this Sunday," I said, practicing my forceful voice while my insides quaked. "The mediator said I had to keep track."

"Fuck you," he mouthed, as he registered the tree again and turned out the door. Molly leaned in for a last kiss. She blew me another as they headed down the drive, her tiny hand a busy wave.

"Fuck you," I whispered back as I watched Hank load her into the car. Harsh? Perhaps, but my relationship with Hank was rife with fear. I know the break-in shook him as well, but at times it seemed he'd go out of his way to taunt me, suggesting I "just get over it!" Despite my need to feel safe, to have all doors and windows locked, he'd often go out late at night after I was asleep, and one time I got up to find he'd left the front door wide open.

"Don't let him get to you," Charlie whispered in my ear as I shut the door. He took me in his arms, pressed me to his chest, lips in my hair. "He's messing with you, just one-up him. Try this. Repeat after me: Suck my dick, Hank, just suck my big dick! Go ahead, say it."

I pushed that sentence out of my mouth, "Suck my dick, Hank!" empowered, I laughed, and said it again.

―――――

By the time our dinner guests arrived that night, I'd put a huge pan of chicken enchiladas in the oven to bake. A vat of spiced wine perfumed the air from its simmer on the stove. Sinatra and Clooney sang from the speakers in the living room. My old pine table was set. A vintage Christmas tablecloth we'd scored at the Rose Bowl, sporting bright red poinsettias, was topped with the fresh evergreen boughs Charlie trimmed from the base of the tree that morning. I'd tucked in extra ornaments and lit candles. Charlie built a roaring fire in the fireplace and the living room walls danced with firelight and the white lights on the tree.

"Wow, looks great in here!" Charlie leaned in for a kiss.

Soon the living room filled with friends, all toting food to share. Ed, dressed in an outrageous holiday sweater and antlered headband, arrived with his famous pear pie. Sam, my boss's son, brought the pot, his spiky hair a festive fringe that fanned several inches above his head, making him even taller than his six-three height. Lacey, a consummate baker, made the perfect rum cake, which she bragged contained an entire bottle of rum, evidenced later when we all swooned after having a slice. My co-worker Lena arrived armed with bottles of wine and champagne. Sam lit a joint and soon pungent smoke hung in the air like the Los Angeles smog.

Mulled wine and marijuana make for a great party.

I'd billed the evening as a tree-trimming fiesta. The coffee table was covered with baskets of art supplies: scissors, glue, glitter, and colored paper; a stack of color copies of photos of our whole tribe from throughout the year; pipe cleaners, colored markers, and shiny holiday stickers—the works. It was up to this crew, stoned and crafty, to add the final flourish to our Christmas tree.

Charlie stepped into the role of host and master of ceremonies seamlessly. He kept the tunes spinning on the stereo and stoked the fire. These friends, all mine, now his by proxy, sat cozy by the fire, while he directed the crafting.

Such a contrast, I thought to myself, as I watched him from the dining room. Hank, always threatened by my friendships, did his best to undermine them. Charlie welcomed everyone and charmed all. He was an equal opportunity flirt.

Lena and Lacey corralled me in the kitchen just as I'd finished concocting the salad dressing. "God, he's cute," Lena giggled, and grabbed for the salad tongs. Petite and stylish, she had cut her hair short and bleached it platinum. Last time I saw her, it was blue. Blond, a definite improvement, set off her chestnut-brown eyes.

"So? How's it going?" Lacey shot me a smile.

"He's fun, and way too young—he's only 23." I felt a rosy flush climb my neck and spread across my cheeks. The two of them registered my blush and nodded at each other, all winks, and grins. "Okay, a lot of fun, but that's all it is!"

———

Perhaps influenced by the enchiladas, by the end of the night, the Christmas tree looked as if it had traveled to Mexico for the Day of the Dead festival. It was festooned with brightly colored cutouts. Lightning bolts, fashioned from silver and gold metallic pipe cleaners, zigzagged from the branches at wild angles. Someone even crafted a skull from tin foil raided from the kitchen.

Once the tree was overloaded, Charlie started folding

paper hats, origami style, from the stack of old copies of the *LA Times* that I saved as fuel for the fire. Ed joined him, and soon all heads were topped with kooky hats. Tin foil stars sprung from pipe cleaner springs. A halo hovered over Ed's head, elaborate architectural antlers over Sam's. The laughter was loud and happy. Hysterical sing-alongs broke out periodically. Wine was spilled. More than one glass shattered.

Everyone had a great time. Except, perhaps, for Charlie's ex-girlfriend, Carrie, the opera singer who was in LA visiting her sister for the holidays. "Invite her," I'd said magnanimously to Charlie when he told me she'd be in town. By the time she arrived, dinner had already been devoured, and all in attendance were solidly drunk or stoned or both. She was a tiny thing, strawberry blond hair in a pixie cut; it was hard to imagine a voice big enough for opera could come from this girl. I welcomed her in, handed her a pair of scissors and pointed to the basket of art supplies.

"We're making ornaments," I said. She looked so uncomfortable, a pained expression on her pert face. Later, I watched her from across the room as she stood with her back braced against the far wall. I remember thinking it must have been awkward for her, a room full of unknown revelers and her ex-boyfriend at the center of it all.

Mercifully, Lena approached her and introduced herself. "How do you know Kate?" she asked.

"I don't," she said. "I know Charlie."

"Oh, how do you know Charlie?" I heard the word boyfriend float over the frivolity as Opera Girl's eyes fell on Charlie across the room. *She still loves him,* I thought. Charlie had greeted her with a hug when she arrived. They exchanged a few words before he was summoned to help secure Lacey's hat, which kept sliding off her head under the weight of décor. I watched Carrie watching Charlie from across the room while he attached wide pink satin ribbons to each side of Lacey's hat with a stapler and then tied a huge bow under her chin, the two of them giggling. Opera Girl left before the party ebbed. Charlie walked her to the door and saw her out. He said something I couldn't hear and then she was gone.

It was long after midnight when the crowd cleared. I trailed through the house collecting dirty glasses and cake plates sticky with rum cake crumbs. I ferried them into the kitchen while Charlie rinsed and loaded the dishwasher.

"Great party, huh?" I said.

"Yeah, really great. Hey, listen, I'm not going to stay over tonight," Charlie kept his eyes trained on the bottom of the sink as if he was speaking to the drain. "I'm thinking I should probably spend some time with Carrie the next few days, while she's in town, you know. It's just a few days," he added. "I promised to show her around."

"Huh?" I said, trying not to care, a tight pinch in my chest, a rock in my throat. "Alright, I guess."

After all, I told myself, *It's just for fun. Right?*

———

Christmas came and went, Charlie in absentia. He called every day to check in, peppering our conversations with "I miss you," and asking repeatedly if I was okay. I'm sure he sensed my distance. I played it cool—aloof. I was busy ignoring the fact he was with his ex-girlfriend, trying to pretend it didn't matter.

A few days after Christmas, Opera Girl flew home to New York, and Charlie called. "Can we do dinner?" he asked.

"Okay. Sure." I was miffed at him and annoyed at myself. I'd missed him.

Two hours later, Charlie arrived with a bouquet of "stoplight roses" in hand. He leaned in for a kiss as he crossed the threshold. "I missed you," he whispered in my ear, lips grazing my neck. I flushed in spite of myself.

I busied myself making dinner and charged him with setting the table. When we sat down to eat, aware of a faint tug in my chest, I asked, "So, how was your visit with Carrie?" I kept my voice light while realizing I might not really want to know his answer.

"Well," he paused. "We broke up for real this time."

"What do you mean for real? I thought you broke up for real before you moved to Los Angeles."

"Well, it was kind of a trial," he went on, "but now it's done." This sentence rang a warning in my head, one I should have heeded, but brushed aside. Something in his manner was a little off, a little cavalier. It's his youth, I reasoned at the time, telling myself it didn't matter. This thing we had *was* just for fun and not for keeps, after all. Still, something worried me into silence.

He leaned over his plate and kissed me—an eraser of a kiss. Before I knew it, I'd danced over that nag of pain—did a tiny jig of adjustment—and as soon as we'd finished dinner, we waltzed our way to the bedroom, a trail of blue jeans in our wake.

Red flags flapping in the breeze.

———

The day Charlie walked through my front door, he was 23, footloose, and a flirt. I was a 31-year-old single mother in the process of divorce. I had a wicked case of PTSD and a weekly appointment with a therapist, a dead ringer for Diane Keaton. In hindsight, she was not the best therapist for me, though she could have played one on TV.

I had already graduated from UCLA and was living in Florence, Italy, while Charlie still in high school, played the lead in his small-town Wisconsin high school play, and rode atop a float through the streets of that town, crown-headed, as Homecoming King.

By the time Charlie was in college studying theater, I had left Florence, landed my dream job at the Corcoran Gallery in Los Angeles, and was living with the man who would become my first husband.

I would guess that on the night that stranger broke into my Venice Beach apartment in my ninth month of pregnancy, Charlie was living in New York City with his girlfriend, and was perhaps backstage at the opera watching her performance from the wings while he plotted his move from east coast to west.

I can't know the exact timing of such things all these years later. But what I do know now is this: by the time Charlie and I met on that day in fall of 1988, though mismatched by age and by stage of life, we were uniquely qualified, like lock and key, to collide and start our mysterious and futile journey. A journey fueled by the wounds we carried through our separate lives. Our bruising childhoods, and broken hearts, the sum of life experiences, which cause two humans to seek a home in another, in a place that is not a home at all.

No stars aligned that day, just wounds.

4

PROVIDENCE

A ll these years later, I know serendipity cuts both ways. The fact that Charlie had arrived in my life unbidden, that he was content to spend time at home with my toddler and me, seemed somehow lucky. Providential.

My career had fallen into my lap in much the same way.

It is not uncommon that people snicker or grin when you tell them you have a degree in Art History. Thoughts fly to perpetual unemployment, courtesy of a virtually jobless field.

A chance meeting on a cross-country flight from New York to Los Angeles gave me the intro I needed. After I graduated from UCLA, I'd flown to New York City to spend a week visiting MoMA and the Met, those American cathedrals of art, bathing in Rothko, Pollack, Diebenkorn, and Hockney.

When I boarded the plane at LaGuardia to head back to LAX and trailed the aisle in search of my seat, I came upon a dapper, middle-aged man, with a full head of foppish gray hair. He was impeccably dressed in wool tweed, complete with a natty bowtie. In his lap, he held a package, wrapped in brown paper, and tied with twine, red stickers at regular intervals alerting: FRAGILE. He held it gingerly, like a priceless treasure.

"I believe that's my seat," I said pointing to the one next to his, in the center despite my request for aisle or window.

"I think you are mistaken," said the man, a slight smile in his warm eyes, still balancing the parcel lightly on his perfectly pressed wool trousers. "That seat belongs to Jim Corcoran." *Jim Corcoran, the art dealer?* I thought. I checked my boarding pass and held it up for him to see. "Ah, Jim must have decided to stay on." He shrugged and smiled. "In you go then," he stood carefully so as not to disturb the contents of his mysterious parcel.

"What's in the box?" I asked, once settled into my seat.

"Nothing that would interest you, my dear girl."

Soon the captain directed the flight attendants to prepare for departure.

"Sir, you will have to put that box under the seat in front of you," the flight attendant said. The gentleman nodded as she spoke though he made no effort to follow her instructions.

"It must be held upright," he said to me, with a nod.

Once airborne, we introduced ourselves, chatted a bit and it turned out I was sitting elbow to elbow with Nicholas Wilder, famed art dealer and gallerist. This man represented nearly all the artists I'd spent four years as an art history major studying devoutly.

By the time our first airborne cocktails arrived, I'd told Mr. Wilder all about my fabulous week in the city. I gushed with enthusiasm over my freshly minted art history degree, my week spent in worship of Mark Rothko paintings, "my version of church," and my plan to get a master's degree in museum studies so that I could work in my field. In turn, he plied me with stories of wild dinner parties thrown in his Manhattan apartment with Mark Rothko, Jackson Pollack, and other greats in attendance. Nearly levitating out of my seat over my good fortune, I was drunk on his stories, giddier with each artist mentioned. Finally, he lifted his brow and nodded at his parcel.

"It's a Cornell box," he grinned.

"Oh my God," I caught my breath as my heart sped up. "I love Cornell." Joseph Cornell, an artist who crafts intricate shadow boxes filled with a carefully composed assemblage of found objects. I conjured the contents of his parcel in my mind's eye. A parrot? A ball? An old bottle? And all curated by Cornell's own hands.

I guess I must have made some kind of competent impression, because by the end of that turbulent martini-drenched flight, Mr. Wilder offered to introduce me to some people in the LA art world. "In fact," he said, "I'll get you a job."

Thanks to Mr. Wilder, I ended up working for the art dealer, Jim Corcoran, whose seat I had miraculously slipped into on that late-night flight.

————

At the James Corcoran Gallery, we handled the cream of the west coast crop. Among them, Ed Ruscha, Ken Price, Ed Moses, Billy Al Bengston, and Chuck Arnoldi. My good fortune: I'd landed in the L.A. art world at a time when west coast artists were overtaking the New York art scene. Wandering the art storage in the back of the gallery, my heartbeat always quickened. The smell of paint, the sight of huge canvases cradled in racks, drawers full of prints and drawings. It was like having an exclusive membership to a private museum. The fact that Jim Corcoran had partnered with famed art dealer Leo Castelli to purchase the Joseph Cornell estate meant I would spend private time with many Cornell boxes during my work there—a tidy circle back to that moment on the plane.

One of my primary duties at the gallery was to monitor the art sales and track the payments to the artists. One artist dubbed me the gallery angel because I made sure the artists got paid before the money turned into that ubiquitous abundance of white powder that fueled the 1980s.

By the time I met Charlie, I had left the Corcoran gallery and taken a job with the sculptor Robert Graham in his Venice Beach Studio. Graham's work, representational bronze sculpture, so singular and exquisite, stunned me with its beauty.

In my early years there, the studio was still housed in a dilapidated old building that loomed over Windward Avenue with its iconic colonnade, just a half block from the unending circus of the Venice boardwalk, with its chainsaw jugglers, fortune tellers, weightlifters, and rollerbladers. Unlike the gallery, which was open to the public, Bob's studio was a private space, secret and walled off from the world.

His studio was a mystical place—cavernous—ceilings cathedral height. Sunlight filtered through skylights and dirty clerestory windows. Dust motes glittered in the haze and mingled with Bob's ever-present cigar smoke. Dimly lit, every surface teemed with wax figures, all precursors to eventual bronzes. Maquettes and models for new and old projects covered tables and pedestals. There were full female nudes, along with sculptural fragments—arms, legs, and heads. It was a laboratory for a mad scientist—a master sculptor.

My office in the old studio was a dark, dusty hovel where I worked daily to create a coherent filing system for the decades-long neglected stacks of paper, some four feet high, that stood atop empty-but-hopeful filing cabinets. I loved being summoned from my tiny office into Bob's studio, though I was often nervous around him. Bob was an imposing figure. Six-foot-two? Three? Four? He was thin and his crisp white shirts hung on his broad shoulders. He was a powerful figure and, as successful men often are, he was complicated.

My days at the studio were varied, and it was never dull. I could just as easily find myself cataloguing documents for upcoming commissions as greeting a who's who of contemporary artists and the Hollywood stars that orbited them. You never knew who might pop by for a visit. One day Han Solo, dressed in street clothes, and the next, a "wild and crazy" white-haired comedian, trailed by a starlet with three names.

Included in my duties—the procurement of contraband Cuban cigars and celebrity pigs.

Yep, pigs...

One day, not long after Bob started dating Anjelica, he called me into his studio. "Kate, I want to give Anjelica a pig for her birthday. One of those little pigs." He smiled through the swirl of cigar smoke that wound through his graying curls.

"Potbellied?"

"Yes, that's the one."

Long before the internet, I searched the livestock section in the *LA Times* classifieds and discovered potbelly pigs for sale in Cucamonga, California, near Riverside.

The day we took delivery, Lena and I watched from the tiny window by her desk as the pig wrangler rang the bell at the huge gray metal door that faced the street. Lena buzzed her in, and we stood in the dark corridor as the woman led the little pig into my office on a leash. It was adorable and still small, a black-and-white-spotted creature with a perfect pink nose.

Anjelica's birthday was still a few days off and it turned out the pig would spend the weekend in my windowless office. Despite being fed and watered by Bob's assistant over the weekend, when I arrived for work the following Monday, the pig had eaten long strips of my office floor, peeling the old pine boards up like tree bark. Had his legs been long enough, he may have ingested the teetering piles of papers—all those contracts for commissions and architectural plans for public monuments— still waiting to be sorted.

———

My closest friends were all members of the same tribe. We all had careers in the LA art scene. Art openings and wild art parties were a given. It was a glamorous life for an art history major.

Charlie's arrival in my life meant I included him in these art events. I'd like to say he fit right in. Charlie's first job in LA was as a studio assistant to the artist DeWain Valentine. Valentine's studio was two short blocks from Graham's—this afforded us daily lunches and midday strolls through the circus on the Venice Boardwalk.

Molly's weekends with Hank, while I dreaded them, provided us with child-free time filled with art openings, dinner parties, and wacky dates. Charlie, short on funds, was a creative dater; I never knew what he'd think of next.

"I've got a plan," he said one Saturday night. "Come on." He threw an old blanket in the car, drove to the local strip mall, and parked in the lot facing the old Culver City drive-in theater. He timed our arrival perfectly, and soon the MGM lion, with its open-mouthed roar, glowered at us from the gigantic screen just visible over the high wall.

"Wait, wait, hold on!" He tuned the radio to a station broadcast out of Tijuana. Mexican talk radio blasted from the speakers. "The Terminator," overdubbed in Spanish, streamed at us from the gigantic movie screen across the street. Charlie pulled the blanket from the back seat, lit a joint, and soon we were tipsy and snuggled in, laughing as Arnold and his cohorts rambled on in rapid-fire Spanish. We made out under that blanket; the windows steamy with condensation.

———

A week later, the Terminator walked into my office, a fat cigar dangling from those big white teeth, hands as big as catcher's mitts. He stopped to fondle the bronze buttocks of a female nude that stood on a pedestal in my office. "Oh, what an ass," he said, smiling at me.

"Hey! Hands off!" I commanded.

After he left, I called Lacey at Chuck Arnoldi's studio, just a few blocks away to warn her he was making the rounds. "I had to tell him to keep his hands off the patina!"

"Already been here," she laughed. "When he buzzed the intercom, he actually announced himself as the sexiest man alive."

"What an ass," we laughed in collective eye rolls.

5

TAR PITS

"So, when am I going to meet Charlie?" My mother's voice traveled through the phone line and landed at the base of my spine. I'd learned that when my mother met the guy I was dating, things got real. She'd never warmed to Hank and was pleased when we split. Charlie and I had been dating almost five months now. He was a near daily fixture in my life. I couldn't put it off any longer.

We met for breakfast at Canter's on Fairfax. The Jewish delicatessen, an L.A. institution, hadn't changed much in five decades. It was always busy, particularly so on Sunday mornings. Mom and my new stepfather, Tim, were already at the head of the line snaking the sidewalk out front when we arrived.

"Mom, this is Charlie. Charlie, Mom and Tim."

"Hello, Mom!" Charlie winked at my mother and held his hand out to shake Tim's. Both Mom and Tim were dressed head to toe in Patagonia. My mother, petite and trim, had traded her designer wardrobe for "urban hiker" when she left my father. That day, she was wearing Birkenstocks instead of

Ferragamo flats. Her perfect Dorothy Hamill haircut was the only thing that remained of her former life.

"Birkenstocks, Mom?"

"They're so comfortable!"

"I think they're cute," Charlie interjected with his best crinkly smile.

"Thanks, Charlie." She nodded at him with a twinkle in her eye and a quick nod at me.

Mom and Tim had married a little over a year ago and they were still in the honeymoon phase. They were cute with each other. I liked Tim, and Mom was happier than I'd ever seen her. Tim was funny, a little goofy even, a hippie who'd joined the Peace Corps more than once, and had, in fact, induced my mother to trade her golf clubs for hiking boots and her Episcopalian roots for Tibetan Buddhism.

The beehive-haired hostess called us in and led us through the noisy clatter of the crowded delicatessen. She escorted us past the usual cast of characters at the counter. We wound around the revolving display cases full of glistening pies and pastries. Past the gleaming deli cases displaying juicy pastrami and deep-pink corned beef, then the bakery counter jammed with knish, kugel, and cookies, all alluringly lit for their close-ups.

The four of us slid into a booth, the pinky beige Naugahyde still damp from a wipe down. I'd worn a short skirt and the backs of my thighs scudded as I slid in next to the pony wall that divided our table from the neighboring booth. The scent of fresh onion bagels and a clatter of plates, the chatter of waitresses calling orders into the kitchen, were all part of the bustled chaos of a Sunday morning at Canter's.

We ordered our food. Mom and Tim steeping their tea while Charlie and I drained hot coffee from our heavy diner mugs. Our waitress arrived and laid a platter of lox, cream cheese, and bagels down on the wood-grained Formica.

"Thanks, Delores!" Charlie said with a wink at our server, reading the name embroidered on her blouse. Delores, buttons straining across her chest, red hair in a bouffant, winked back at Charlie and smiled at me.

"He's a flirt, this one!" she said, leaning over him to fill our mugs with more coffee. The four of us, like breakfast architects, assembled our bagels. Mom spread the tiniest bit of cream cheese on her plain bagel, followed by a single slice of smoked salmon. I slathered my big bialy with cream cheese, thick as cake frosting, studded it with capers, added sliced tomato, and piled glossy lox on top, followed by a squeeze of lemon and a sprinkle of salt.

My mother looked askance at my creation. Her surveillance of my eating habits was a holdover from my chubby childhood —one that had me on diet pills at age ten.

"What, no onion?" she whispered, a slight nod in Charlie's direction.

"No onion," I smiled.

"Tim, has anyone ever told you that you look just like Robin Williams?" Charlie said. Tim was adorable, with scruffy curls and a beard; he wore wire-rim glasses over blue eyes, the corners creased with deep smile lines.

"Yeah, I get that a lot," Tim explained that just last week in Santa Monica, a guy had chased him down the Promenade, pages in hand. "Mr. Williams, I wrote this with you in mind, perhaps you'd give it a read?"

"Charlie, what do you do for a living?" my mother interrupted.

"Geez, Mom."

"No, it's okay," Charlie said.

"Kate said something about theater?"

Charlie smiled. "I have a theater degree from Drake University, it's a small, exclusive private school in the Midwest," he chuckled. This tagline, tinged with sarcasm, always followed the mention of his alma mater.

"I'm working for an artist in Venice, just a few blocks from Kate, but not for long. I'm going to get a job in theater, maybe even set design for film." He described his new night gig at the Groundlings Theater on Melrose, running lights and the soundboard two or three nights a week. "I'm hoping to make some connections."

"And where are you living?" my mother asked.

"I share an apartment with a guy in Venice," he said, smiling at her.

"Kate says you're an English teacher?" Charlie listened intently as my mother described her classroom, her students, and her schedule. He asked her questions, fully engaged in her rambles. Mom, charmed by his attention, grew more twinkly, and animated over the course of breakfast while Tim and I looked on—amused.

After we consumed our quota of lox, bagels, and cream cheese, we trekked across the street to the LA County Art Museum to take in the Netsuke exhibit at the new Japanese Pavilion. The four of us hiked across the vast palm-treed parking lot, spikey shadows under foot, blacktop ablaze with winter sun. Charlie and Tim kibitzed like old friends a few yards in front of Mom and me. Charlie glanced back at me periodically as if to ask, "How am I doing?" I shot him a nod and a reassuring smile.

"Oh, Honey!" my mother whispered, "Charlie's adorable, so charming."

I looked ahead to Charlie, where he walked in his faded jeans, white Converse high-top sneakers, and blue button-down shirt. "I want to make a good impression," he'd said as he got dressed that morning. I found his efforts to please endearing.

"So handsome," my mother continued.

Too handsome? I wondered. This question nagged me. Why would someone so young and so hunky want to hang out with me, eight years his senior, a single mother with a toddler? This guy was golden, his smooth skin browned in the sun just as quickly as mine burned and blistered red. I'd always gone for dark-haired men, was never drawn to blondes. He was a boy of a different color.

"Too bad you didn't marry someone like him in the first place," my mother said. "Maybe he's your second chance."

"Mom! I told you, I'm done. I'm never getting married again!"

I had chased all thoughts of a second chance with anyone far away, let alone a future with Charlie. I'd spent my childhood believing if I didn't want anything, I couldn't lose it. Better to not be disappointed, or worse, heartbroken.

"Never say never, sweetheart." my mother smiled and patted my arm. "He's great!"

There you had it. Everybody loved Charlie. Molly, my friends, and now my mother. In those days, I was so unsure of myself, so full of self-doubt, I let the opinions and assurances of friends and family override my own feelings. In Charlie's case, the sense something was off was like an itch I could not reach. So back then, I reassured myself—if everyone who cared about me thought otherwise, I was obviously wrong.

Mom and I caught up to Charlie and Tim. They had stopped in front of the tall wrought iron fence that surrounded the La Brea Tar Pits, a huge pond of bubbling tar, slick with shiny black goo, some bubbles so large they reflected the sky and the palm trees at our backs. Across the way, giant faux mastodons, like Disney figures, lolled in the sun on the tar-blackened banks.

"Wow, this is so cool! I've heard about this place!" Charlie said with childlike wonder. "Let's go in." He led the way into the enclosed viewing area, a platform high above the ongoing excavations below. "All this history!" I heard him say to my mom, she and Charlie up ahead chatting as Tim and I stood a few feet away on the overlook.

"He's a keeper, Kate." Tim put his hand on my shoulder and squeezed. We caught up to Mom and Charlie, and all four of us stood and watched while down below, archeologists chiseled away in the hunt for old dinosaur bones, long ago submerged and hidden like dark secrets.

Charlie looked at me and smiled. His eyes traveled down into the blackness of the pit and I watched his smile fade to an expression thick with thought.

6

90210

"Hey, look at this!" Charlie was scouring the classifieds in the Santa Monica Daily Breeze over bacon and eggs one Saturday morning. We were sitting at my pine table, dining room windows open to the front porch, the morning breeze scented with jasmine and tinged with bacon. "Beverly Hills High School is looking for a technical theater director!" He read the job listing to me, eyes lit with excitement.

By Friday of that week, he'd had his first interview.

"So? How did it go?" I asked over dinner. I'd roasted a chicken, stuffed it with quartered lemons, garlic cloves, and fresh rosemary sprigs from the garden, and made Charlie's favorite—crispy roasted potatoes—all in anticipation of the good news.

"Great! I think they really liked me." He detailed the job description with excitement as he munched a bite of potato. He'd be the tech director for all the high school shows, design all the sets, work with the kids, and teach them to run the lights and sound. "It's my dream job!" Then he paused as a shadowed thought crossed his face. "They asked me the funniest question, though."

"What was that?"

"They wanted to know what I'd do when all the high school girls started falling in love with me." He stared at his plate and speared a bite of salad.

"How did you answer that?" I asked, aware of a pinprick in my chest. This question echoed my own concern. I'd been a high school girl once and the allure of young single teachers was not lost on me. I watched his face and waited for his answer.

"I told them it was a non-issue, a strict boundary I'd never cross." *Good answer*, I thought. "And besides, I told them we were getting married!"

"You told them *what*?" I coughed, choking on a bite of chicken.

"Let's get married."

"You're kidding, right?

"I'm serious Kate, let's get married."

"Charlie, I've told you, I'm never getting married again. Ever." I reached for my water glass, took a huge swig, and chased that bite of chicken down my throat.

————

It was August 1989 and we'd been together almost a year. I knew enough to know I was in love with Charlie, but I also knew I would not marry him. He was too young, too cute, and in my estimation, not fully cooked. Besides, I was terrified to marry again, to make a second mistake. I was better off single. Just Molly and me.

There were other reasons. After Opera Girl flew back to New York City, Charlie and I established a near-daily routine, which included near-nightly sleepovers. One night after six months of "going steady," he came over after his gig at the Groundlings Theater full of stories about Robe Girl. He called her Robe Girl because she wore a robe in her act.

"I really like her," he said, from the wing chair, the floor lamp beside him illuminating a faint smile.

"You like her?" I shifted in my spot on the sofa.

"Yeah, I think I'd like to ask her out."

"Ask her out?" His comment winded me. I was so busy falling for him while trying not to. "You want to date? Her? What is it *we* are doing then? You're here in my bed every night. You tell me you love me and now you want to date *her*? Who are we to each other?"

"I do love you, Kate. I love you, and I love who I am when I'm with you. I love Molly too. But you've said you won't ever get married again. I want my own kids. I thought you didn't love me in that way. I thought..." His voice trailed off in search of his next sentence, eyes downcast, those damn long lashes fanning his cheeks.

For one long week, we went around and around this Robe Girl thing. In the end, he declared his love for me and swore I'd be his one and only.

———

In those days, I was good at falling into things. I had a knack for letting circumstances decide my fate. My first marriage was a case in point. When I returned to LA after my second year in Italy, Hank picked me up at the airport. We had dated for just a few weeks before I had moved to Florence.

"Where ya gonna live?" Hank asked as he hefted my suitcase into his car.

"Beats me."

"How 'bout my place?"

Some four years later, I had finally broken things off with him, knowing the constant criticism that felt so much like home was no longer the home I wanted to live in. He pleaded with me and promised to change. "Come camping," he'd said. "We'll talk things through." Magic mushrooms, a canopy of stars, a roaring campfire beside a rush of river, his seed took root, and the baby I'd longed for begged to be born. I married him for the sake of our child despite my reservations, knowing divorce was always an option.

You'd think I'd learn, but I hadn't.

Charlie's roommate was getting married, and his fiancé was moving in. Charlie had to move out. We discussed his housing dilemma, my dicey finances, and the cost of renting two places vs. combining our resources to pay for one. Besides, Charlie stayed at my house nearly every night anyway. Why not?

Looking back, I'm sure my need to feel safe factored into my decision. Sleep had been elusive since the break-in, and I felt more secure with Charlie there; he took his role as my protector fiercely. So, despite my refusal to marry him, living together seemed to make perfect sense. This was long before I understood that decisions taken lightly held consequences—consequences that would send fault lines through decades.

Years later, I can see it. A hurtling train. A wreck in the making.

———

Charlie got the job at Beverly Hills High School. It was September 1989.

Our little house on La Salle Street in Culver City quickly

transformed into the Boys and Girls Club of West Los Angeles. Every weekend, the kids of 90210—some grandchildren of Hollywood greats—would slum it at our house. I'd unfurl old beach blankets on the front lawn in the wavy shade under the Jacaranda tree. Our grassy front garden, rimmed with a short wooden fence, kept all those geeky theater kids—like lost sheep —in the confines of our front yard. Charlie was their shepherd. Happy high school chatter filled the garden as paper plates slung low with huge slices of pizza, stringy cheese oozing off the sides, made their way around the yard, followed by soda cans and paper napkins.

There were kids of all shapes and sizes, more girls than boys in this gang, some of them tomboyish, others lithe and willowy. They all hung on Charlie. They were all "tech kids." They ran light boards and built things; they painted sets and made costumes. They were the crafty counterparts to the young actors and actresses who longed for a life on the stage, some of whom would go on to real careers thanks to talent or parentage.

In those days, I felt like a den mother. I was the backstage manager. I greeted the kids, ordered the pizza, passed out the paper plates, and then I went inside to fold the laundry or clean out a closet. Charlie was the guy out front. I admired the interest he took in these kids, his role as counselor and confessor to his flock of adoring high school students. He seemed born for this job.

Two of these kids stand clear in my memory all these years later. One, a boy, tall and gangly, was painfully shy, particularly lost and needy. Charlie counseled and encouraged him with the care of a mentor. The other, a girl. She was boisterous, loud, and a tad chubby. I read her manner as a screen for her insecurity. She always arrived late, made a bouncy entrance, albeit awkward, and she always brought gifts: lattes from Coffee Bean and Tealeaf, one for me and one for Charlie, and always a toy or a book for Molly.

Molly loved these Saturdays. She had a starring role—little sister to all those teenagers. They passed her around like a baby doll, she hung on their hips, rode on their shoulders, and climbed into their laps while they sketched plans for sets and set changes.

Molly loved the boisterous girl best of all—Mallory.

7

HORSE AND CARRIAGE

Love and marriage, love and marriage
They go together like a horse and carriage
This I tell you, brother
You can't have one without the other...

Charlie's first proposal and my first *no* were just the beginning. From there, the proposals collected like the seashells Molly and I kept in a dish by the door. Some came like missives, others like salvos, still others delivered in song.

Molly, at three, was obsessed with Frank Sinatra. She desperately wanted to meet him. "But only if he's wearing that bathrobe," she'd say, pointing to his picture on the CD cover. "It's called a smoking jacket," I explained.

"Okay then, I want to meet him in his smoking jacket."

Charlie taught Molly all the words to "Love and Marriage." Sometimes they'd sing it along with Frank, the stereo turned up loud. The two of them looked like a vaudeville act, bobbing up and down like an old calliope while I watched—amused—from the couch. They sang it at breakfast, sometimes at lunch, and always at night while we all did the dishes. Molly, standing on the red kitchen stool doing her best to dry the plates, loved the "horse and carriage" part best. She sang that phrase loud with a wooden spoon held up like a microphone to her lips, a grin on her full moon face.

Later, when Molly was asleep, Charlie would persist. He'd hum the tune, his eyes full of love and sex, and then he'd whisper-sing, "Come on, Kate, you can't have one without the other."

———

I found my therapist, Allison, through a referral when my state funds for counseling at the Rape Treatment Center at Santa Monica Hospital ran out.

Her office, in an imposing two-story Georgian brick colonial, fronted by substantial Corinthian columns, was an architectural anomaly where it sat on a busy commercial street pockmarked with used car dealerships and fast-food restaurants in Culver City.

The day of my first appointment, I was at the foot of the grand central staircase, which had thick white banisters down each side, ending in carved volutes, like something out of a Hollywood movie set, a staircase for Grace Kelly or Cary Grant. A forty-something woman, with straight brown bangs over kind brown eyes, came down the stairs and my heart did a little loop de loop. *Oh my God*, I thought, *it's Diane Keaton. I love Diane Keaton!*

She walked up to me and held out her hand. "You must be Kate. I'm Allison," she said. Years later, I would run into the real Diane Keaton while trailing through an antique store. "Allison? What are you doing here?" I realized my mistake when the real Ms. Keaton looked at me, puzzled, shook her head, and smiled.

Three years and countless appointments later, my personal Diane Keaton, dressed in menswear just like Annie Hall, sat across from me and swiveled in her ergonomic office chair.

I plopped on her sofa, the same sofa Charlie and I had sat on together a few months back when he'd asked to come to therapy with me, in hopes to understand my refusals and change my mind.

Today, I held my hands palm up in front of me, all ten digits fanned out, and tallied his proposals. "Charlie asked me to marry him again. That makes nine. Nine times *officially*," I said. I'd lost count of the sung ones.

"What is it, Kate? Aren't you in love with him?"

"Yes, I'm in love with him. That's not the problem."

"What is it then?"

"I don't know, Robe Girl? Opera Girl? I'm not sure. I have a nagging feeling that I can't trust him."

"Kate, that was more than three years ago. You've been living together for two now. He loves you; he's committed to you. His devotion to you and to Molly was so evident to me when the two of you came for your couple sessions."

I didn't doubt his love. Not really. And I loved him, wanted him, wanted his levity and his love in my life as friend and lover. But not as a husband.

"I can't put my finger on it. He's such a flirt. I just don't trust him. His age—maybe he's just too young to settle down," I said. "Oats to sow, you know."

Allison leaned forward in her chair. "Kate, consider this, I believe it's your fear of intimacy that keeps you from his love. I urge you: say yes. Trust will grow in time."

So filled with self-doubt, not knowing if I could—or even should—trust my gut, I trusted others with my decisions. At the time, I reasoned Allison must be right; she was the professional after all.

Trust would grow in time.

I can't remember that tenth proposal. Spoken or sung? Who knows? But what I do remember is this: Three years and ten proposals later, I said, "YES."

———

I planned my wedding with Charlie carefully. My first one was so haphazard. I'd married Hank on the Ides of March, four months pregnant, with a smallish bump beneath my lace. Our wedding at the Self Realization Temple in Malibu, on a rare cloudy day, was well attended. I remember it raining, but now I don't think it actually did. It just felt rainy. A Hindu yogi, wrapped in Creamsicle robes, blessed us, and showered us with orange azalea blossoms. Azaleas? *Why not rose petals?* I'd wondered. I should have known. In my experience, when roses appear, blessings follow.

This time, I took no chances. I did my research and learned the meaning of flowers. Apparently, azaleas sent in a black vase signified a death threat. Reading this sent a shiver clear through me. This time, I made sure there were roses. Lots and lots of roses.

Saint Francis by the Sea, the old stone chapel where we chose to wed, sat high on a cliff in Palos Verdes, south of Los Angeles. My parents were married at the same altar where we would take our vows. As an infant, I was baptized there in another ivory gown. On that day, my favorite uncle, Mitch, just fifteen at the time, held me beside the baptismal font. The view of the ocean from this place had always held a deep significance for me.

I credit my Uncle Mitch with my love of the ocean. This

story is one of those family legends I've heard so many times it is embedded in my memory. With my mother's permission, my uncle bundled me, fresh from the hospital, into a big navy-blue pram, gleaming like a brand-new Bentley. He pushed my carriage out to the edge of those cliffs, where they dropped off into the ocean. He lifted me, swaddled, from the carriage and held me up to show me the sea. I imagine in that moment my infant eyes taking in the blue Pacific, all sparkle and gleam, a universe of stars like the one I'd just come from. I still feel it now, that mystical wonder, and to this day my soul settles at the ocean's edge.

Charlie and I married in my favorite month beneath a shimmer-blue October sky. A gentle breeze wafted through the eucalyptus trees; their leaves rustled above our heads.

Molly, at four, paved our path with rose petals, her pale pink gown, tied with a wide white silk sash in a perfect bow. Charlie asked the Beverly Hills High School a cappella choir to sing. Their angelic voices filled the old stone walls of the chapel with Gregorian chants, while friends and family witnessed our union.

We said our vows: I will. I do. For better or worse, my pledge. I would stick this one out no matter what. I said those words out loud that day and, deeper still, in my heart.

Two marriages, okay; two divorces, no way. This was my solemn vow.

8

UNPLANNED PARENTHOOD

*Look out for Mr. Stork, that persevering chap, he'll come along
and drop a bundle in your lap.*

Santa Monica, 1992

I sat in my chair with a nervous shiver despite the clammy
warmth of the crowded waiting room. A low hum of
language buzzed throughout the room as the sun streamed
through the clerestory windows, spotlighting a banner on the
far wall: *"Planned Parenthood proudly serves people of all ages,
national origins, races, and sexual orientations."* The orange
chairs backed up to the walls were filled with women who told
that story—all ages, all shapes, sizes, and colors.

With a clipboard balanced on my blue-jeaned knees, ball-
point clamped between shaky fingers, I filled in the blanks with
careful penmanship.

Number of pregnancies: 2
Number of live births: 1
Number of abortions: 1

Number of miscarriages: None

As I wrote a bold 'I' next to the word "abortions," a somersault rolled my stomach. Long before we were married, Charlie and I faced our first real crisis by way of egg and sperm: an unintended pregnancy.

Back then, when I told Charlie I was pregnant, he said, "Great! Let's get married." (Proposal Number Five? Six? Seven?) Nope, no way. I wanted another child, but I did not want a pregnancy to force another marriage, so I chose. Charlie had gone with me to the Beverly Hills clinic. He held my hand while I squeezed his. Later that afternoon, he made me chicken soup and kept the hot compresses coming while I cramped and bled in our bed.

Today was different. This pregnancy was planned. I was almost thirty-six and figured time was not on my side. That, plus the abortion, caused an incessant worry over my ability to conceive. We wanted a child, a bold YES to this union of ours. I longed for a baby, and Molly begged for a little sister with the same persistence she had pled for a kitten.

This is it, I thought at the sight of the little blue cross that appeared on my pee stick that morning. I kept the sign to myself and once Charlie had left for work, and the sitter arrived to care for Molly, I beelined to the clinic with nervous glee.

Ushered into to the exam room, I wrestled the baggie holding the pee stick from my purse and held it up for the nurse to see. Her cropped gray hair fringed her round face, deep gray eyes flashed concern. "Kinda faint," she shrugged. "The blood test will tell." It seemed the little blue cross had faded since morning. No worries, I knew the signs. Bone-deep exhaustion. Missed period. Sore breasts. The nurse checked my vitals, took my blood, and promised to call as soon as the results were in. I drove to work with my happy little secret tucked into my purse, confident of the outcome.

Later that day, I started to bleed. When the nurse called with the happy news to confirm the pregnancy, I explained I'd painted three rolls of toilet paper red with evidence to the contrary.

Within five short weeks, that familiar exhaustion had strong-armed me to the couch. *Can't be,* I'd thought to myself, counting the weeks on one hand. Besides, I reasoned, I hadn't had a period since the miscarriage. Like disobedient teenagers, we'd ignored the doctor's orders to "refrain from relations." Nevertheless, new tests confirmed I was pregnant again, my hormone levels high.

This pregnancy was a long slog of morning, noon, and night sickness that required close proximity to a bucket or the bathroom for eight long months. Still, we prepared for Finn's advent with joy and excitement. The day of my ultrasound, Charlie sat happy, holding my hand, studying the screen for a sign. We could hardly wait to tell Molly the big news.

"Molly, you're going to have a baby brother!" we told her over dinner that night.

"Oh no! Not a boy! Boys are so hard to train!"

Luckily, Charlie had another surprise for her that night. "Molly, our next show at the high school is called The Grapes of Wrath. The cast has asked if you'd like a role as one of the Joad Children?"

"Really? I get to be on the stage?" she danced in her chair. "Ooh, yes!"

On the day of the first rehearsal, I picked Molly up from her kindergarten classroom and was greeted by her teacher. "Molly is so excited," Mrs. Gates said, as I grabbed Molly's jacket from the hook by the door. We turned and walked the four blocks toward home.

"Oh, Mother!" Molly raked her hand across her brow. "Today is the first day of my life on the stage!"

With Molly's excitement barely restrained by the seatbelt in the back seat, we drove from Culver City to Beverly Hills High School. I sat in the theater and watched the rehearsal. All the high school kids, those who had roles on the stage and those that worked behind the scenes with Charlie, were thrilled to have Molly in their midst, and all were excited when she announced we had a new baby on the way.

9

MEETING MARINA

"Welcome, everyone! Shoes off, please." Our instructor greeted us as we trailed through the door that opened into her living room. Jenny was an OBGYN nurse who taught Lamaze in her home. She was tiny, five-foot-two, her thick glossy brown hair streaked with silver and in a perfect bob. Her house looked like an illustration pulled from an Old English fairy tale. She had a magical way in the garden. Tiny roses in snowy drifts cascaded the stucco walls of her little cottage. Tulips and daffodils filled the front yard in spring. Her house looked like a place where children would live happy childhoods forever.

I'd been to Jenny's house before. First for Lamaze, when I was pregnant with Molly, and then after Molly was born. Jenny had come to the hospital, having heard about the break-in. She held my hand and smoothed my hair. "You will survive this," she said, her soft gray-green eyes like summer ponds I wanted to drown myself in. At the time, I didn't believe her. "Come to my new mother's group," she'd said. "It will be good for you."

Back then, when Molly was an infant, we came together every Thursday. Eight new mothers gathered to discuss our new-mother struggles: diaper rash, colic, sleeplessness. We'd sit cross-legged on this same living room floor in a circle, jiggling babies in our laps—some of them fussing or gurgling, some mercifully sleeping.

One Thursday, a mother stood, jostling her baby in her arms; she was obviously disturbed and anxious to share. "I heard a horrible story from my mailman," she said. "A young woman in the neighborhood, pregnant with her first child, was raped."

I felt the urge to leave my body, to escape this unwanted reality. I had the sensation of flying up and hovering in the corner of the living room. Had the door been open, I would have flown out. There was only one person there who knew the story. Jenny.

She nodded at me from across the room. I felt the comfort of her grey-green eyes, the longing to sink to the floor of that pond. Instead, with her encouragement, I forced my way up. "That was me," I whispered. "It wasn't *someone*. It was *me*." A collective gasp circled the room.

With Jenny's support, I unleashed the story I wished was not true.

"Remember the heat wave last July?" All eight mothers, pregnant then too, sighed remembering the heat, and nodded yes. "It was twelve days till my due date..." I was hot, couldn't sleep. It was after midnight. Hank was late. I'd opened the windows, but there was no breeze. I craved a bath with cool water. I ran the taps, stripped, and climbed in. I couldn't wait for the water to fill the space around my hot, pregnant body. Up to the brim, the clatter of the water cascading into the tub blotted out all sound. I closed the taps. Buoyant relief. And then: a sound—a creak in the floorboards that didn't belong.

I leaned forward in the tub and I saw him. He saw me. What I saw did not compute. An intruder. I froze. I pushed myself into the back of the tub and willed myself to disappear. But there was no disappearing from this. I screamed. He lunged. His hands, a tourniquet around my throat, ever tighter to silence me. I screamed still. He yanked me by my neck, up and out of the tub, slamming me and my unborn baby to the floor. Again and again, he bashed my head into the tiles, my brain bouncing in my skull. The more I screamed, the tighter his grip—a stranglehold sure to pop my eyes from their sockets. My pregnancy, the enormity of it, was of no consequence to him. He wanted what he wanted, and he would take it.

"Oh my God, Kate." This sentence echoed around the room, tears streamed every cheek.

"Did they catch him?" asked one young mother.

"Hank came home in the middle of it. When the rapist heard the door open, he yanked himself free and ran back through the bedroom, leapt out the window, onto the sidewalk, and into the arms of my upstairs neighbor. He'd come down after he'd heard me screaming. The neighbor caught the man and beat him."

"What did Hank do?" another asked.

"He saved the guy," I said.

"Saved him?" One of the mothers gasped. "My husband would have killed him."

I shared the rest of the story in a flood of tears. Relieved to let it out, to have them as my witnesses. "My neighbor told me he would have gladly killed the guy, but Hank had pled with him to stop. Instead, the two of them sat on the rapist until the cops arrived."

With urgency, I went on. After the police, the ER, the rape kit, the charting of bruises and contusions, at long last and only after begging for it, the nurse arrived with a fetal heart monitor.

"Louder please. Louder!" I demanded. And finally, the sound—
the holy sound of my unborn daughter's heartbeat broadcast
over the din of the emergency room.

With Molly still asleep in my lap, I continued, explaining
that later that night, I'd stood for what felt like hours in a Motel
6 shower. "No amount of water could wash this," I said. "When
I finally climbed into that hotel bed at four in the morning,
Hank blamed me. He told me it was my karma that brought the
rapist through our window."

"Karma?" The word repeated like an echo around the
room.

"Yep. Our marriage mostly ended then."

———

Now, nearly six years later, I sat on Jenny's floor again,
pregnant with my second child; my second husband behind
me, his stocking feet pressed against my lower back, applying
constant pressure just where I needed it. Another child,
another man, another group of mothers. Another me.

We assembled ourselves. Three couples, as if playing duck,
duck, goose, in a ring around the living room, all of us perched
on calico cushions on Jenny's luminous hardwood floor.

"This will be fun, we're a small group," Jenny said. "Let's
start by introducing ourselves."

Sue and Steven went first, all brown hair and brown eyes.
Steven, attentive; Sue, a little shy. Midwestern transplants, they
planned to return to Chicago to be near family after the baby
was born.

Next up, Marina and Nick. They had moved to Los
Angeles from New York; both worked in the entertainment
business. Nick was tall and thin, with a spiky mop of blond
hair, big black glasses, and a distracted air, fidgety and uncom-

fortable in this environment. Marina, tiny aside from the basketball in her lap, had a wild fringe of thick black hair, a frizzy halo that she fiddled with—one moment twisting it up into a knot on top of her head, the next unleashing it to fan out like a frothy headdress past her slim shoulders. She had an offbeat style—quirky—with an infectious laugh that was a little raspy, sandpapered. She was funny and acerbic. I was instantly drawn to her savvy and her sarcasm. Marina was someone I wanted to know.

Our turn. "Hi, I'm Kate, and this is Charlie."

"Kate's done this before, but I'm a newbie," Charlie added.

"My back is killing me," I said. "Anyone else?" Two hands shot up. Charlie demonstrated his back-brace technique; Steven immediately took position behind Sue, and she sighed with relief. Nick didn't budge. Marina clucked her tongue, shot me a sideways glance and blew a little puff of air up her face, lifting a fuzzy curl off her forehead. She cocked her head in Nick's direction. He sat oblivious.

"Man, I gotta pee," Marina announced to the group with a throaty giggle. "Nick, help me up please?" Nick stood and heaved Marina off the floor, and as soon as she was down the hall, he headed toward the door.

"Hey guys, gotta make a quick call," he said, excusing himself. I watched Nick through the window; his long-legged strides to his black SUV parked out front. He opened the passenger door and picked up the car phone in the center console.

Peals of laughter rang out from the bathroom. Marina half-waddled, half-ran back into the living room, laughing. "Oh-my-gawd! What the hell was that?"

"Oops!" Jenny laughed. "I forgot to warn you about Bill!"

"Bill?" Marina, still laughing, held her hands beneath her quaking belly.

"He lives on the other side of the bathroom door." Jenny and her husband had adopted Bill, a big green parrot, when they were in grad school. At the time, they thought it would be funny to teach Bill a few choice words. Bill had a filthy mouth, and a trip to Jenny's tiled bath was always met with a loud wolf whistle, somehow perfectly timed to the moment you dropped your drawers. Then as you took care of business, Bill would recite a litany of expletives—cunnilingus and fellatio, just a couple.

"Oh. My. Gawd!" Marina laughed; her accent tinged with a bit of east coast. She looked out the big picture window. "Shit! Is he on the phone?" Pissed, she stormed out the door, yelling from Jenny's front porch, "Nick! Get back in here!" Nick slunk back in the door, apologized, and glared at Marina. For the rest of the evening, tension sat between them like a third person.

Later, over herbal tea and cookies, Marina confided that she'd warned her husband that if he didn't stay present, there'd be hell to pay.

For the next several weeks, we met like this. Charlie entertained the group while supporting my back. Marina sat on her own, unsupported by Nick, who, always cutting some deal, would excuse himself at regular intervals to make calls from his car. Marina's dark eyes flashing a shiny blaze in his direction.

Marina and I, both seven months pregnant—big and wide, our bellies full of boys—bonded on that hardwood floor. Our friendship was fast, a rushing river. When we finally gave birth, in July of '93, our boys made their entrance into the world on the very same weekend, in the same hospital, just one day apart.

Marina's Timmy and my Finn would spend their early days swaddled side by side while Marina and I exchanged confidences and compared sleep patterns, diaper rash remedies, and breast infections.

10

LEAVING LA

July 1st, 1987—the night I was raped—changed me. The PTSD created by that event meant my days were filled with anxiety, panic attacks, and a heightened sense of danger. It also served to separate me from my belief in a benevolent God. The bubble of protection I'd believed I inhabited had been blown to bits.

In the days and months following the rape, I developed an insatiable need to ingest as much bad news as possible. I was obsessed with the local late-night news; it provided me with a steady diet of dire fright. Tales of people in terrifying circumstances were my bedtime stories. Rapes, murders, kidnappings, no crime shocked me. Looking back at it now, I know I was trying to integrate the violence done to me. A nightly confirmation that horrible things happen every day, just like the horrible thing that happened to me.

Fast forward thirty years and the sound of running water still unnerves me. I fill the tub fully clothed, trailing the house, checking locks on doors and windows. I often panic in the shower, fear the noisy cascade will blot out sound—a sound I desperately need to hear. To this day, a hand—however tender —on my throat, undoes me. Thirty years on, I feel deep compassion for myself in these moments. I accept these things are part of how I live in the world. Always alert to danger.

———

In March of 1991, the news of Rodney King's brutal beating by officers from the Los Angeles Police Department outraged and sickened me. Footage of the unbearable brutality aired in a continuous loop and tensions between whites and blacks were at an all-time high. A heightened sense of danger reignited my PTSD. By 1992, five years after the rape and one year before Finn was born, the daily horror show, a parade of rape, murder, and mayhem, had worn thin.

I was at work at Robert Graham's studio in Venice Beach on April 29th, 1992, the day the Rodney King verdict was announced. The reaction was immediate, like a bomb blast; it rocked the city, just as I'd feared.

I'd been on edge for days. "This town is going to explode," I said to Allison just two days earlier while I sat quaking on her sofa. My nerves buzzed with fear. I felt it in the fine hairs on my arms, the feathery wisps down the back of my neck. Every cell signaled the coming danger.

"I think we have to attribute this to your PTSD," she'd said. "I sense that everything is going to be fine." Looking back, I know Allison wished the best for me, but she got so much wrong.

News of the riots sent the guys on staff at the studio scurrying to secure the premises. Bob rushed into my office, panicked. He was concerned about his Porsche, which sat exposed in the drive on Windward Avenue.

"They'll set it on fire if it stays in the driveway," Bob said, cigar smoke chasing his head as he paced the length of my office. "Drive it over to Billy Al's; he said we could park it there." I looked at Bob. *Really?* I thought. *The Porsche? Electric Avenue? In the middle of a riot?*

In those days, Electric Avenue divided Venice into two distinct halves—the rough neighborhoods to the east and the slow creep of gentrification moving west, toward the ocean. This funky little beach town was a hotbed of crime in the late 80s and early 90s, and Billy Al Bengston's compound, a fortress behind high walls, sat in the crosshairs. Not to mention, it was a mere block-and-a-half from where I'd been raped.

Dutiful despite the danger, my coworker, Lena, drove the Porsche while I followed behind in my white Honda wagon, hands gripping the steering wheel to steady me as a tide of panic flooded my chest.

Though it was less than three minutes door to door, the drive felt like miles. The air was electric and strange, the way it feels before a tornado hits. Sirens shrilled through the air. Police cruisers flew by, lights awhirl. Our path crisscrossed with cars piloted by panicked drivers, all running for cover. Lena skidded into the short driveway and cracked the window just wide enough to pound the buzzer. I idled behind her, shaking.

A cop car screeched to a diagonal halt cutting off traffic on Electric Avenue in both directions. "What the hell are you girls doing here? You're gonna get yourselves killed! Outta here! NOW!"

When the gate to Billy's compound finally rolled open, Lena hit the gas hard. She parked the Porsche, leapt into my car, and we sped away, the cop screaming at our backs, "Go! Go! Go! Go!" I dropped Lena back at the studio and peeled off down Venice Boulevard in the direction of Molly's preschool.

What I saw through my windshield that day felt like a 3-D screening of Mad Max and Blade Runner, all rolled into one slow-motion nightmare. Bricks flew from the hands of angry mobs crowding every intersection. Cars swerved up and around other cars and onto the sidewalks, if necessary. No one stopped at a single light for risk of being hit by those flying bricks that crashed through countless windshields. I raced toward my destination in a nonstop weave. My heart pounded the bounds of my chest; my shirt soaked through with sweat. By the time I pulled into the parking lot behind Molly's preschool, the school's director had barricaded the kids inside the six-foot wooden fence that enclosed the campus. She handed Molly to me through a narrow crack in the gate but pled with us to stay with her and shelter in place. I needed to get home, certain that the house on LaSalle Street was safer than this mix of commercial buildings that sat exposed on Venice Boulevard—targets for gasoline and the toss of a match.

We made it home, plumes of smoke visible in the distance. I closed all the curtains, locked all the windows and doors, and checked the answering machine. Charlie had called to let me know he was leaving Beverly Hills High School. "It's 3:45 now. I don't know how long it's gonna take, but I'll be home as soon as I can. Keep the doors and windows locked, I'm on my way!" This was so long before cell phones, it's hard to remember the unbearable chasm of silence that opened when you hung up a phone.

I sat Molly at the dining room table and busied her with coloring books and crayons. I flipped on the TV set in the corner of the living room, sound low, and picked up the phone to call friends and family to check on their welfare and whereabouts. Everyone accounted for, I fed Molly a hasty supper of mac and cheese as helicopters thudded the airspace over our neighborhood. My head and heart prayed silent prayers. Protect us, please. Bring Charlie home safely.

By the time Charlie made it home that night, I'd settled

Molly into her bed, read Goodnight Moon three times, and stayed by her side until, at long last, she fell asleep.

"Thank God, you made it!" I cried as Charlie came through the door. We held each other hard while he described what he'd encountered on the long drive from Beverly Hills to our house. Fires, sirens, bricks, and sticks pitched through the air like javelins.

"I've got a plan," Charlie said breathlessly, as he pulled our giant map of the city of Los Angeles from the bookcase in the living room. I watched as he spread the map to cover the coffee table in front of the sofa. The ceiling flickered a jagged light over our heads, mirroring the fractured images of our city awash in violence as they scrolled on the television screen.

We huddled cross-legged on the floor at the coffee table. Charlie drew a circle on the map around our neighborhood with a fat black sharpie, an imaginary wall with a two-mile perimeter. "If the fires stay outside this circle," he pointed to the ring, "we shelter in place. If they cross over, we grab Molly and run." We kept watch all night. With the newscaster as our guide, we plotted each new fire on that map, with a blaze-orange magic marker. I finally dragged myself to bed at three in the morning. Charlie spent the night on the couch, a vigilant eye on the TV screen.

The next few weeks were as close to living in a war zone as I have ever come. Tanks and Humvees, loaded with uniformed National Guard, rumbled through the neighborhood. Snipers in riot gear kept watch from the rooftops of Target and Safeway at the local shopping center. And worse, the riots reactivated the seismic tremor of PTSD lodged in my bones and blood, courtesy of that stranger who'd climbed through my window just two weeks before Molly was born.

———

By the time the Northridge earthquake threw us out of bed in January of 1994, Charlie had been lobbying hard for a move to Portland. Our son, Finn, was six months old and I had just lifted him to our bed for his four am feeding when the shaking started.

Charlie flew from the bed to Finn's crib and dug frantically through his covers to rescue him. "I've got him!" I called. "Go get Molly!"

The sounds in that darkness were chilling. Our wedding china, loosed from the hutch in the dining room, crashed down the walls. Glasses were thrown from the kitchen cupboards, shattering as they hit the linoleum floor. When the shaking stopped, the power was out, and my honor scout husband herded his family out into the driveway. He'd set up a jumble of lawn chairs lit with a flashlight. He wrapped our shivering bodies and bare feet in blankets that he'd dragged from the linen closet. We sat in the January cold while patrol cars made their way up and down the streets of our neighborhood, shining searchlights through the dark.

"Everyone okay?" the cops hollered at our driveway huddle.

"All okay!" we called through the dark.

Once the sun came up, Charlie went to survey the damage before calling the all-clear.

With the kids corralled on the sofa, we spent hours in cleanup mode. We shoveled all the broken bits of our belongings into the trash and returned the contents of our kitchen cupboards to their rightful places. A handful of jars had fallen from the spice rack into the goldfish bowl on the counter below.

"Hey look!" I said to Charlie as he swept broken glass from the kitchen floor. I pointed to our fish, Golda, and Meir, as they swam unscathed in and out of Spice Islands.

"Kate, it's time. We need to leave."

"They have earthquakes in Oregon too, Charlie."

"It's not just earthquakes, Kate. I don't want to raise our kids here. And just think, we could afford to buy a house there," Charlie reasoned.

Charlie had an aunt and uncle who lived in Portland, and we'd gone for a few visits over the years. They lived in the leafy enclave of Laurelhurst in a big Portland Foursquare. Their house looked like something out of an episode of Bob Vila's *This Old House*, a show we watched with religious rigor. On our visits, we spent our days there driving through neighborhoods with names like Irvington, Alameda and Grant Park.

"Stop the car!" I'd cry at regular intervals, jumping out to snap photos of picturesque schoolhouses and quaint vintage bungalows—no two alike, yet all perfectly stitched into a magical quilt that spread down shady streets under a canopy of trees.

"The schools are better," Charlie added.

"What about our jobs?" Charlie loved his job at Beverly Hills High School. And I loved mine. I made a good salary working for Robert Graham. Not to mention my network of friends and family.

Despite Portland's charms, I resisted.

———

"Charlie wants to move to Portland," I said to Marina over lunch that next week. We compared earthquake stories as we juggled two wild six-month-olds, Finn and Timmy were in our laps, busy banging spoons on the tabletop like rock band drummers.

"Oregon? He'd leave his job?" she asked puzzled.

"He says he wants a better place to raise the kids. Wants to buy a house."

"What about *your* job?"

"I know. But we'll never have enough money for a down payment here. I don't know, between the rape, the earthquake, and the riots...maybe it's time for a change."

"Well, ya know, I've been to Portland and it's kinda cool there," Marina offered.

"You have?

"We own some investment property up there." Nick and Marina's success in the entertainment business afforded opportunities beyond my reach. "Act-u-ally," she continued, pronouncing each syllable for emphasis, "I kinda like it there, it's quiet and it's de-lic-ious-ly green. If you do move, Timmy and I will definitely come visit."

———

Three months later, on the day I witnessed a high-speed chase through the streets of Venice, I knew I was done. There were no cops in sight. Just hot rods. A gold metal-flake Chevy Chevelle, lowered, scraping the blacktop, sparks flying, chassis nearly airborne over speed bumps, was being pursued by a red Olds Cutlass, also low and sparking. They weaved in and out of traffic, ran every red light, and nearly sideswiped my car. I steered north on Ocean Avenue, my heart slamming my chest. Every cell screamed. Something terrible about to happen. I crouched down behind the wheel, and waited for a hail of bullets. I imagined getting caught in the crossfire. Instead, I watched as a bloodied body was thrown from the back seat of the speeding Cutlass onto the sidewalk, just as I drove by in my car.

The reverberation of all bad things thrummed my cells like an out-of-tune Stratocaster, distortion turned high. My ears rang with fear. My body was wracked with sobs and PTSD-fueled hyperventilation. I pulled my car to the curb and sobbed. I had to leave this place.

"Let's do it," I said to Charlie that night over dinner. "Let's move to Portland."

———

In June of 1994, at the end of the school year, Charlie handed in his resignation at Beverly Hills High School, and I gave notice at the studio. I was ready to leave LA, but reluctant to leave my career, which now included the honor of my hand-print forever embedded in the FDR memorial in Washington D.C., and the privilege of working on Bob's MOCA TORSO project. A program he'd created after the riots to train ex-gang members in the art of lost wax bronze casting.

"Oregon?" Bob chuckled through his cigar smoke with a wry smile. "What are you going to do in Oregon, Kate? Farm?" He nodded at my outfit. "You've got to stop wearing those ridiculous overalls."

I'd added the oversized overalls to my wardrobe after Finn was born, paired with a crisp white blouse, a silk peony corsage —a post pregnancy fashion statement.

"You don't like my new uniform?"

"No, I don't." Bob smiled and shook his head.

"Baby weight," I smiled.

"Best of luck to you, Kate." He sighed and grinned at me through the garland of smoke encircling his head.

"Thanks, Bob. It's been an honor."

11

I THINK I FOUND OUR HOUSE TODAY

My husband's ardent voice met my ear with a tickle through a network of phone lines that ran the length of the west coast—from Los Angeles to Portland, Oregon.

Charlie had gone ahead to Portland earlier that summer to look for work and a place to live. I'd stayed behind with the kids to pack things up and shut things down, to wrangle with Molly's father and the court system for permission to move my daughter north to the verdant state of Oregon, where it sat just above California promising home ownership and a lush green peace.

"It's in Grant Park!" Charlie chimed into the phone. "Remember that big park we walked through? It's just a block away!"

"Fireplace?"

"Yup, great mantel, and all the woodwork's painted white, just the way you like it."

I missed my husband. The summer alone in LA had been brutal. The countless trips to the courthouse to battle with Hank over Molly's move were bruising. Settled in the end,

Molly would spend one long weekend every month and eight weeks of every summer with her father in LA, and I would never have another Christmas with my daughter. At the time I was crushed, but fair is fair. I was moving Molly to another state and away from her father. Still, I fought hard for Christmas, my favorite holiday. Yet, in the end, if I wanted to leave Los Angeles and start a new life with Charlie in Portland, this was the price I'd have to pay. A sacrifice made in the name of hope.

"Hardwoods?"

"Yup! And crown moldings!

"Dining room?"

"Uh huh. Plenty of room for that big ol' table of yours."

I sat at one end of that table now, in the dining room on La Salle Street. The house was mired in chaos—burgled by my own hands. Packing boxes colonized my once-loved rooms. Today's face off, a towering mountain of dishes and glassware, might as well have been Everest.

It was late September, hot and smoggy. A box-fan rattled at the end of the table, its shaky breeze fingering my neck and flirting with a stack of crispy newsprint that had see-sawed my fingers with paper cuts. I gulped my bottomless beaker of iced coffee—too much sugar, too much coffee. My heart beat off kilter. My thick blond hair was unwashed and knotted on my head with a number two pencil. I stunk and yet I shunned the shower. I ached, but ignored the siren call of my tub, and the Epsom salts that beckoned from beneath the bathroom sink. Can't stop now. What would I do with Finn?

Finn. Barely one, still crawling, was a hyperactive speedball. He could cover more territory in a split second than a fly fleeing a swatter. From where I sat at the far end of my table, I could see his chubby arms and legs, my little locomotive, as he chugged in and out of packing boxes. I'd arranged the boxes, sealed, and labeled, in a maze on the living room floor and draped them with old sheets and blankets. It was an unsightly tent city in our living room, created just to keep him occupied. His diapered rear popped in and out at regular intervals. "Peek a boo!" I called when he poked his head out and flashed me with his drooley grin. Nope. Can't stop now.

"Any word on that job yet?"

"Not yet. Don't worry. Hey, you okay?"

"Exhausted," I said.

"I miss you, Kate. One more week and you'll be here! Please don't worry," he repeated as he rang off.

I *was* worried. In fact, my worry over our financial situation was considerable. With both of us unemployed, what little we had saved would disappear quickly. And despite my resolve to leave the "bad" LA, the "good" LA still had a lover's hold on me. This city was my Jekyll/Hyde. Yes, it had dealt me horrors, but it had also gifted me with an incredible education and a fantastic career. I knew this gritty city like a tattoo on my skin, and I knew people. Years of work in the LA art community, meant I had vast connections and deep friendships.

The closer my departure date loomed, the greater my doubts grew over my decision. In those last days, even the clogged freeways and the hazy sunshine—okay, smog—were beguiling. Still, the lure of a quiet life with my adoring husband and my kids, who deserved to grow up in a home of their own, living a life free from the constant crime and chronic stress of my big crazy city, pulled me north with a promise of peace and safety.

———

"Finn will learn to walk here," I said to Charlie a week later. We stood on the deck looking out into the backyard of the house on Knott Street, my head nestled on his shoulder. I breathed in his soapy skin and nuzzled his scruffy chin, his arm snugged around my waist.

"Look! The perfect branch!" I said, pointing skyward. An enormous walnut tree shaded most of the yard. I could already see the swing hanging from its sturdy branches; hear Molly and Finn, their peals of laughter as we pushed them up and through the clean Oregon air.

"And look," Charlie said, "back there next to the garage. It's sunny! Perfect for your vegetable garden."

There it was, that bubble in my chest, an almost impercep-tible burble that dared me to hope. Somewhere in my child-hood, I'd adopted the belief that to want, to hope, was to tip my hand, to give myself away. It was far safer not to want anything; this was my rule. What you didn't want, you couldn't lose.

"Wow, it's like a tunnel up here," I gasped when we climbed the stairs to what would be our bedroom. The cavernous room ran the entire length of the house, fifty feet of hardwood floors and a ceiling that cried out for skylights and dormers. The big double hung windows at either end of the room struggled, but failed, to shed light on its shadowy center. *Nothing that lamps won't fix,* I thought.

"Think of it as our 'Tunnel of Love,' Kate!" Charlie leaned me into the wall with a deep kiss and then waltzed me the length of that love tunnel.

"God, I missed you," he said. "Happy?"

"So happy."

12

WE DID IT

"We did it! We rented the house on Knott Street!" My husband lifted his glass.

"Yay! Yippee!" A chorus rang round the table. Wine glasses collided with pints of beer and plastic sippy cups sloshing milk.

We sat, a mismatched bunch, around Scott and Sara's shiny Ethan Allen-ish dining room table. Scott, Charlie's uncle, was a bushy-bearded Dead Head who bore a distinct resemblance to Jerry Garcia. I found him odd and unnerving; I attributed this to his outsized brain. He was brilliant, teaching black holes and string theory in the math department at the local university. His wife, Sara, was a strait-laced lawyer, with a neat brown bob and warm brown eyes. She wore conservative suits from the racks at Talbots. How these two fit together, I did not know.

Across the table sat my husband. How I'd missed him. His tousled blond head slanted just so; his eyes beamed a crinkly smile on me. That spotlight smile singled me out. I always felt sparkly and adored in that beam. I sat sweatered against the cold, my wooly cuffs tugged down over my fingers. Ten toes, like ice cubes, bundled into wool socks and boots. It was late September, and the Pacific Northwest sun set early. Days grew shorter, nights cooler. It would take five long years for my thin LA blood to acclimate.

Scott and Sara's big old house was cold and drafty. They never lit the furnace till the end of October, a Portland badge of honor. The house, for all its glorious bone structure, screamed for attention. I sat at the dinner table longing to help Sara redecorate. In my memory, the only art on the walls were metal-framed Grateful Dead posters—Scott's proud collection. The furniture, it seemed to me, were all castoffs from college dormitories; an amalgam of oak and brass, with a dash of wood-grained Formica thrown in. And then there was the dog hair. Scott's joke: "We don't vacuum so that the kids can make dog-hair angels on the hardwood floors..."

Across the table sat my sweet Finn, perched in a blue plastic highchair positioned next to Emma, his cousin, in one of her own. They were about the same age. Both their trays were littered with the remains of un-sauced pasta. Their chins and cheeks gleamed with a buttery sheen. Courtney, Emma's big sister, pouted in her chair. "I miss Molly," she whined as she pushed her salad from one side of her plate to the other.

"I miss her too," I said. "She'll be here soon." Molly had stayed behind until we got settled. I'd argued with her father and the lawyers against this plan to no avail. She would start first grade in her new school here in Portland a month late.

Sitting next to Courtney, where Molly should have been, was the only non-family member at the table that night. The Boisterous Girl—Mallory.

Mallory had been one of those Beverly Hills theater kids— the gushing girls and eager boys that orbited Charlie at our house in Culver City on the weekends. She'd sent me cards and notes all summer long. They contained words of encourage-ment—It won't be long now—you'll be here soon—Charlie misses you so much. A little odd, though at the time, I'd appre-ciated the friendly gesture. The fact that she'd chosen to go to school in Oregon seemed a coincidence.

Mallory raised her glass. "To Kate and Charlie. Congratu-lations! I'm so happy for you!" she gushed in her aw-shucks kind of way, her shoulders shrugging a quick nod to her ears. Mallory was upbeat and bubbly. Back in LA I'd grown accus-tomed to her giggly presence. Her voice entered a room long before her body did. She had a head of thick brown hair that bounced and kept time with her voice, which was loud and sing-songy in a valley girl-LA way. She always came bearing gifts; I suspected her insecurity required that she arrive with swag—her ticket in. Like an arctic ice-cutter, her prow was a cardboard tray of Starbucks Frappuccinos, a book for Molly, a Tonka truck for Finn. Tonight, was no different.

The kids fidgeted in their seats. Finn and Emma draped themselves with spaghetti and Courtney begged to be excused. "I'll keep them occupied. Come on cuties!" Mallory grabbed a shopping bag from the built-in sideboard in the dining room where she'd placed it earlier that evening. Corralling the kids from their seats at the table, they all paraded through the wide foyer into the living room and convened around the coffee table. She reached into the bag and pulled out a brand-new coloring book and crayons for Courtney, and tins of freshly minted Play-Doh for Emma and Finn.

Charlie and Scott cleared the table and beelined down the basement stairs to Scott's "office," where he kept his stash. A stinky, pungent, skunky smoke floated up the stairs through the basement door and into the kitchen. Sara kicked the door shut with her sneakered toe and filled the kitchen sink with lemon-scented bubbles. Steamy condensation fogged the window above that soapy pond. I grabbed a dishtowel and slid Marvin Gaye into the CD player that sat on the counter. *"What's Going On"* rang through the kitchen.

"Who invited Mallory?" I whispered to Sara.

"No one. She showed up here this afternoon, just before you and Charlie got back, with gifts for the kids. They were so happy to see her. She's been such a big help with them this summer. I kinda felt I should ask her to join us."

Mallory attended Lewis and Clark College, ten miles away and clear across the river, a good 30-minute diagonal drive from Laurelhurst to campus. She'd rented a three-bedroom bungalow a block away from Scott and Sara, on the very same tree-lined street, and filled the extra rooms with roommates. Apparently, she'd wasted no time introducing herself as our family friend, offering her services as a babysitter.

Mallory's choice of housing perplexed me. "What college kid rents a single-family home in a neighborhood filled with well-to-do families and school-aged children?" I asked.

"Yeah, I admit, it is kinda weird, but she's been a godsend this summer."

I'd watched her during dinner, her glimpses at me, at Charlie. She watched him watching me. True, he did not return her glances. If anything, he shunned them, at times wincing at her jokey dinner quips.

"Sara, do you think something's going on between them?" I whispered.

"Oh God, no way! Charlie barely tolerates her."

"Well, it's clear she has a crush on him," I whispered.

"Maybe so, but who doesn't?" Sara grinned. "Nope. Charlie's been miserable, he's missed you and the kids terribly. Besides," she said, "I would have seen it. He's been living here with us all summer long."

But there it was, that faint warning, a nearly imperceptible shiver in my gut. Like a fishtail flip on a lake—a flash—there one second and then gone.

13

HOMEMAKING

A paint-spattered CD player blasted Bonnie Raitt from its perch on the carved mantle above the fireplace in the house on Knott Street. The empty house echoed her reedy voice; that steady beat fueled us toward the finish line. Tomorrow was move-in day. We would make this house our home.

We had spent the week as a song and dance team of paint and polish. I scrubbed every surface while Charlie coated every stick of trim with the color of the whitest clouds. The house tanged with the scent of fresh paint and Pine-Sol. We were down to the last room, giddy and exhausted. Our forearms and fingers were freckled with paint. My hair was tied in a messy knot on top of my head, and spiky blond escapees bopped to the music. Charlie's head bobbed too; his sandy waves were caught in a blue bandana. The two of us sang loud and rolled the walls of our new living room the color of clotted cream.

"Let's give 'em something to talk about," Charlie bent to load his roller, and on the way back up, he danced a sidestep, leaned in, and planted a nibbled kiss on my neck. My skin brailled and my knees did that little buckling thing they do.

"Hey, keep painting or we'll be giving our new neighbors sumthin' to talk about." I nodded into that tickle and out to the street. The big picture windows fronting our new house were bare and wide open to the late afternoon sun. That sun threw shadow branches on the walls through the trees; they danced in the wind and sent slanted light across the hardwood floors.

———

Early the next morning, the house was empty and expectant. I paced the hardwoods, my footsteps echoing on the floors. I kept watch out the wide front windows. October breezes blew a confetti of leaves through the autumn air and peppered the sky like ticker tape. The diesel rumble of the moving van shivered the roadbed, announcing its arrival. Out onto the front porch, I ran.

"Here!" I waved my arms above my head. "They're here," I called to Charlie, through the open front door.

Like a little kid on Christmas, I'd been waiting for this day.

Truth was, long before that green and yellow Mayflower van pulled up in front of the house on Knott Street, my busy brain had worked overtime. I had arranged all the furniture in the confines of my skull long before those burly boys, in their matching green jumpsuits, carried the couch through our new front door. Like a Hollywood director, I pointed and shouted—"Right here! That goes over there, please!"—as each chair, every dresser, bed, bookcase, and my big pine table crossed the porch and made their entrance. Once those deliverymen were tipped and gone, Charlie and I made a few adjustments and fell like timber into the down sofa, where it sat facing the fireplace just as I had imagined it would. Our view was cluttered with boxes, but no matter. We smiled, high-fived, held hands and huffed a long exhale. And then, like a rerun of an old sitcom, Finn took up right where he left off. Reunited with his magic castle, he crawled in and out of the cardboard boxes—his turrets and towers—and flashed his best wet grin.

"Pizza?" I said to Charlie.

"Pizza," he smiled. We paraded to the kitchen, I picked up the phone and placed our order, while he grabbed a couple of beers from the fridge.

———

The next morning, Charlie trundled down the stairs, sleep in his eyes. I handed him a cup of coffee.

"Thanks," he took a sip and smiled. "I'm starved."

"Pizza?" I slid the cold flat box from the fridge.

"Pizza!"

I'd been up for hours. "What do you think?" I held our old bulletin board up to fill an empty spot on the wall between the stove and the back door. "All the kids' artwork, right here?"

He swigged his coffee, eyed the spot, shook his head. "I like it better over there." He pointed to a spot in the nook. I shrugged, disagreed, and set it down on the floor. This would be an interesting process, creating our first home together in this house on Knott Street. In LA, he'd moved into mine. This home would be ours—a collaboration.

I opened boxes, lifted plates and glassware from their newsprint nests and filled the kitchen cupboards. The phone rang. Charlie ran to answer.

"Portland Opera needs my help with the show this week-end," Charlie held his hand over the receiver of the wall phone that hung in the nook. A flash of disappointment registered somewhere in my chest—a hard black bead rolled up between my shoulders.

As a child, I'd decided that to survive life unscathed I would have to be like the grasses that grew by the lake in the High Sierras, where we spent our summers. I watched those reeds bend in the mountain breeze, sometimes clear down to the surface of the lake. When the winds gave way to calm, the grasses would rebound, standing tall, unbroken. The winds of my childhood? My father's long and frequent absences traveling for business which registered as a parade of monthly abandonments, and meant missed birthdays, piano and dance recitals. This combined with my mother's chronic depression which often kept her in bed, left me as the oldest, feeling responsible for her care, and required I look after my little sisters.

I would have to weather Charlie's absences too, and perhaps in hindsight, I was inured to them, predisposed, like a frog in slowly heating water. No clue my froggy life was in danger.

I sighed, hands on the small of my back, bending backward into that nag of pain. I looked left, then right. Our new home was engulfed in a sea of brown boxes. And then I did that little thing I do without even realizing that I'm doing it. I adjusted. Shifted. No expectations meant no disappointments. Like those grassy reeds, I bent.

"Take it," I sighed. "We need the money."

"Ya sure?"

"Go. Go."

My husband ran up the stairs, came down dressed, grabbed his tool belt, planted a kiss on my cheek and jangled out the door. Our team of two became just one. Just me. And then just as quickly as that black bead formed, I slipped it on a silken cord and transformed it into a pearl of opportunity. All the decisions were now mine. I'd hoped we'd make this house a home together, but my brief downshift to disappointment quickly upshifted to gift. I was familiar with this place, this ability to adapt, my childhood resolve to do it on my own. I would place every lamp, every picture, every mirror. And I'd do it unfettered and alone, all on my own, no discussion necessary.

Job one—that bulletin board. As soon as Charlie was out the door, I headed for the kitchen, grabbed my hammer and hung it right where I wanted it, in the spot by the stove.

———

Next day, Charlie went off to help out at the opera again and—wham—I sunk another nail into the wall like a woman who knew what she was doing. That afternoon, I hung the last mirror on that nail over the entry table next to the front door. Eyeballed it for level and caught sight of myself. "You're a mess!" I said to my reflection. My hair was stringy dirty, my face a map of fatigue. A long hot bath was the next thing on my 'TO DO' list.

Too late. As if on cue, Sara carted Finn through the front door. He leaned into me from her hip and made a smooth transfer to mine. His sweatered arms squeezed my neck.

"Mama!" His toddler thighs ringing my waist, I kissed the chub of his neck. He wiggled in my arms, scrambled down my leg and crawled off in the direction of his new room.

Sara handed me a big bouquet of orange mums. "Here's to your new house."

"Thanks, Sara, they're beautiful. Hey, thanks for taking him today, I got a lot done," I said, heading into the kitchen.

"Charlie's still working?"

"Yep."

"Where are the boxes?"

"Out back. Flattened!" I pointed out the French doors at the back of the kitchen. I filled the cut crystal vase, a wedding gift, with water from the tap and arranged the mums just so. I carried them to the big pine table where it sat in its new home and surveyed the dining room with satisfaction. Table. Hutch. Chandelier. The freshly painted walls, a deep golden ochre. Those orange mums sang against that gold in the late day sun.

Sara followed, "Lord, Kate, we still have boxes we haven't unpacked, and we've been in our house for five years!"

"Molly arrives next week, gotta get it done. Tea?"

"Can't. Next time?"

I walked her to the door. She glanced at the living room one more time, shook her head and was gone.

By Sunday, just three days after we moved into the house on Knott Street, I had done it. I had made this house a home.

14

THE HOUSE ON KNOTT STREET

Molly skipped the block and a half to her new school. I strove to keep step. We kicked at the crispy leaves that papered the sidewalk; they made a rustling crunch under our sneakered feet. It was the third day of Molly's first week in her new school. Hollyrood Elementary was a low-slung midcentury building that sat snug at the edge of Grant Park, sheltered by towering Douglas firs, huge maples, and elm, all Crayola colors—goldenrod, burnt orange and sienna brown. The sky was clear and cloudless.

"Oregon, oh Oregon, I love you, my Oregon!" Molly dropped her backpack, twirled her best pirouette, and threw herself into a freshly raked mound of leaves where it sat in a neighbor's yard. She fanned her arms and legs up and out at her sides, her blue eyes wide and filled with sky. "Look, Mommy, I'm making a leaf angel! Oh, Mama, it's so beautiful here, and it smells just like pancakes." She was right. The autumn here smelled syrupy sweet. The decay of fallen leaves laced the air with the scent of maple.

I reached for Molly's hand. She grabbed for mine, and I

pulled her up, my little wood nymph. I plucked the leaves and twigs from her hair, a mass of tangled yellow that cascaded over her shoulders, down to her waist. She smoothed her dress and straightened her knee socks just as we heard the first bell ring.

"Let's run!" We arrived at Molly's first-grade classroom breathless. I kissed her head and plucked one more twig from her hair. She flew to her seat, plopped down in her chair, and beamed a smile back at me. I blew her a kiss and turned toward home. One block later, I stood across the street from our new house, and paused to take it in.

The trees on Knott Street met in the middle. They held hands overhead, weaving a leafy green canopy that would shade our summers and lace our autumns with a blaze of gold. Our house on Knott Street stood sturdy and tall; it anchored us firmly in the middle of our block and graciously faced us south towards the sun.

Clad in wide clapboards painted gray; the trim layered with creamy paint the color of marshmallows mixed with nougat. A steeply peaked roof with a millwork sunburst, supported by two fat columns, hung hopeful over our broad front porch and created the perfect stage, front and center, for all our comings and goings.

Home.

My hunt for a true home had been a lifelong endeavor. In high school, I'd hoped home was a Pentecostal Revival Church. *Not it.* In my late teens, I dreamt home might be the perfect nunnery. *Not it.* At nineteen, I attempted to make a home in a commune in the Colorado Rockies run by a Charles Manson lookalike. *Nope. Definitely not it.* In my early twenties, I finally found my true home in Italy, and had hoped to stay in Florence forever, but joblessness chased me back to Los Angeles. LA *was* a home but, in the end, it ran me out.

This house on Knott Street would be home at last. I was

right to bring Molly here, I thought. All that fight and fury with Hank was worth it. This *will* be a good place to raise my children. We *will* be happy here.

There it was—that hope bubble—it bloomed in my chest. I folded all hope for home into that house—and into my husband as well.

15

THERE'S A REASON IT'S SO GREEN

Molly was my fairy child. She lived in a land of enchantment. She talked to flowers and sang to bugs. When she was two and toddling, we'd go for hikes in the Santa Monica Mountains, the air full of sage, her five little fingers like a daisy in my hand. She'd spy a weedy flower along the sunlit path, slip her hand out of mine, and crouch down to touch its petals. Then, like greeting a long-lost friend, she'd whisper lengthy sing-song conversations, her tiny voice like chimes on the breeze.

So, it didn't surprise me when two days before our first Halloween in Portland she announced that she wanted to be a fairy hummingbird. "Of course," I said. Finn was easy. He wanted to be a fireman. He already had a yellow rain slicker and the perfect pair of red rubber boots. I bought him a fireman's hat, bright red like his boots, from the costume display at Fred Meyer, and his costume was done.

Molly's transformation was not so simple. It sent me on a scavenger hunt through craft shops and fabric stores and kept me up late into the night. I set up shop in the dining room on the big pine table. My sewing machine floated in a cloud of iridescent tulle and feathers: pink, blue, purple, and turquoise. I sewed each feather on a glittery leotard. I stitched more feathers onto wings, a wire armature Charlie sculpted from two coat hangers and stretched with remnants of shimmery nylon stockings. I stitched tiers of tulle into a wide grosgrain ribbon waistband, sewed the last feather to that billowed flounce at three in the morning, then climbed the stairs and dropped, half-dead, into bed.

———

"Oh Mommy, I love it!" It was late afternoon on Halloween and Molly had donned her feathered leotard and tied her tulle skirt around her waist. She darted through the living room into the bathroom to admire herself in front of the full-length mirror. "I need my wings!" I followed her in, wings in hand, and sat down on the edge of the tub.

"Molly, honey, hold still." I worked to guide her arms through wide loops of elastic, hiked the wings up and around her shoulders, tugged at the wire, arranged them just so and there she was, a fairy hummingbird.

"Thank you, Mommy." She eyed herself once more in the mirror, hugged my neck with her glittery arms and kissed me on both cheeks. And then, in an aura of her favorite colors, she flitted through the house.

In all our visits to Portland—count five—before we made our move, I had never seen one bit of rain. Not a sprinkle, not a shower, not a drip, not a drop. Call it luck, or trickery, or as I have come to suspect, a willful act of citywide deception designed to lure us in. No rain for us, just a thick blue carpet of sky. A brilliant, impossible, crystalline blue, dotted with cartoon clouds, pure and white, afloat above our unwitting heads.

The rain arrived on Halloween.

"It's gonna be a wet one, folks!" the Channel Two meteorologist spouted from the television screen in the corner of the living room. I looked skyward from the big picture windows fronting the house. Thick dark clouds crowded the horizon. They mounted their attack. Shadows darkened the living room walls. I switched on lights to fight the gray.

"I'm afraid the rain will start just as the kids head out for Halloween," Mr. Channel Two, prophet of doom and gloom, taunted from the screen. "It will be a drenching rain, folks. Winds upwards of 20 mph with gusts to 35 at times...all in all a rough night for your little ghosts and goblins..."

Despite the forecast, we prepared. I poured miniature Milky Ways into my giant wooden salad bowl and set it on the entry table next to the front door. All those tiny chocolate galaxies awaited the arrival of neighborhood storm troopers and assorted sleeping beauties.

Charlie bundled Finn into a hooded sweatshirt and threaded his short arms into his shiny slicker, booted his feet with red rubber and handed him a length of green garden hose. Finn beamed; he'd begged for that prop all week long. "Nice touch," I said to Charlie.

And then it began.

A drip. A spit. A splatter.

The rain flew. It torpedoed slanted, steely sheets at the house and the street out front.

"Are you sure you want to go out in this?" I asked my husband.

"It's Halloween, what's a little rain?" Charlie grinned; his blue eyes bright. Then he turned and headed up the stairs to our room.

"You'll have to wear a coat, honey," I said to Molly.

"Noooo! A coat will ruin everything!"

Charlie bounded back down the stairs dressed head to toe in a bright yellow rain suit. Ever the honor scout, my husband was always prepared. A weather geek from Wisconsin, he could watch the cable weather channel for hours on end. With Finn snuggled in his lap, Molly at his side, they'd recite the names of cloud formations. "Cirrus, stratus, cumulus..."

"Where'd ya get that?" I laughed at his rain gear. Charlie beamed and from behind his back, he produced a giant golf umbrella. "Ta-da!" He'd been waiting for this day.

The rain beat the roof and rattled the windows. A wall of water hit the road; torrents threatened to crest the curbs on Knott Street. Fierce winds howled and whipped the trees, limbs threatened to snap.

I pointed out the window at the deluge. Charlie shrugged a smile. Molly and Finn grinned and danced before the door.

There they were. My crew. Finn, a shiny yellow sun to Molly's billowy pink and purple fog, and Charlie, the biggest kid of all, outfitted like a 19th-century schooner captain prepared to lead the charge.

"Trick or treat!" they chorused.

I shook my head. Out the door, they went. I watched from the window, dry and warm. Finn on Charlie's hip, Molly's arms a shimmer around Charlie's waist, a huddle of color under a blaze-orange golf umbrella. That orange sail, worthless in the wind, fought Charlie's grip and won, blown inside out by the time they got to the end of our front walk.

Not fifteen minutes later they returned in defeat. Molly featherless and shivering, her pink ballet slippers destined for the trash. Charlie still smiling, "Wow, now that's some rain."

I marched Molly and Finn straight to the bathroom,

plugged the tub, filled it deep, stripped them bare and in they went.

"Warm up," I said. "Hot chocolate on the way!"

———

That first year in Portland was a long dreary blur, wet and unrelenting. The rain that started on Halloween dragged fall into winter and winter into spring.

I learned a new vocabulary. Weather terms that were useless and nonsensical in my sunny homeland. Showers meant one thing—they turned off and on without warning. Rain another—continuous with no end. And then that term—sun break. My brain did a mental double-take at that one. Growing up in California a sun break was something my mother enforced. "Come in from the sun! You'll burn!" she'd yell from the window over the kitchen sink as my sisters and I turned red and blistered in the pool.

Here in the Pacific Northwest a sunbreak was more hide and seek, something the sun did when for a brief and fleeting moment it broke through that gray blanket of sky and shouted "Hey! Remember me?" and then just as quickly as it had flashed that golden beam, it retreated into hiding. A merciless tease.

I tried to make the best of it. I made dinners and I made drapes. I built fires and lit lamps. Lots and lots of lamps. I collected them at garage sales and thrift shops and placed them in every corner of the house, on every flat surface, in every room. They did their best to fight my gloom.

I had been warned. If only I'd listened.

While still in LA, at a sunny poolside cocktail party—all sunglasses and whiskey sours—a Portland ex-pat who'd overheard our plans to move, told me flat out that I was crazy.

"There's a reason it's so green!" he chided, with a clink to my glass and a shake of his head, "You'll see. You'll be sorry." I'd laughed it off.

But here's the thing:

I hated the rain.

It paled my skin. It frizzed my hair. Even the pinholes that pierced my ears bubbled and crusted with infection. It made every errand a bludgeoning water ballet, a merciless game of dash and dodge. Add wind to the mix and my umbrella—that fragile contraption—blew inside out. Or caught an updraft, skittered, and flew off into the wet gray sky, leaving me drenched, dripping, and defenseless. Add a squirming toddler, a bag of groceries, and a stroller to this mix. Impossible.

It was halfway through our first July when summer finally arrived. I knew I was in trouble—deep, deep, trouble—when despite the blue-green crystalline perfection that was Portland in the summer, I could not shake my sense of dread. October was coming. It laid in wait. It sloshed my bones and soaked my cells. I slid into a sadness I could not shake. It painted me gray despite the blue.

The rain was coming.

The rain would ruin everything.

16

NEW CLOTHES FOR OLD FURNITURE

Our first year in Portland, we cobbled a living out of Charlie's odd theater gigs. One week he painted sets for the opera, the next he ran lights for a local theater or helped out at a high school auditorium. It was a hodgepodge crazy quilt for a family with two young children to support. But we did it. My job search turned up nothing. The art world I belonged to in Los Angeles was non-existent in Portland. *What had I been thinking?*

I had a hobby. While still in LA, I'd taught myself to sew. My kids had wrecked my linen sofa, and in desperation, I taught myself to make a slipcover. No matter I had flunked Home Economics in junior high, screwing up the A-line skirt assignment on purpose so I would never have to sew again. It turned out, that I could sew; could even draft a pattern. And in the end, I succeeded. Once the word got out, I made slipcovers for friends and friends of friends, for extra cash, while still working for Robert Graham in his Venice studio.

Because it was Portland in 1994 and shabby chic was all the rage, I thought I could capitalize on the trend. I phoned the only person making slipcovers in Portland at the time, an elderly lady who specialized in tight-fitting slips in floral chintz.

"Shabby chic?" The aging seamstress coughed her smoker's cough into the phone when I called to inquire. "Listen, honey, there's nothing chic about shabby." Bingo. I had a niche.

"Chairwear. Whaddya think?" I asked Charlie one morning over breakfast. "Chairwear—new clothes for old furniture."

"Catchy," he said distractedly, shoveling forkfuls of scrambled eggs into his mouth.

"I figure we'll pay more in childcare than I could possibly make sitting in a gallery selling bad art at five bucks an hour."

"Go for it." Charlie grabbed his tool belt and jangled out the door.

A dear friend designed my business cards. She made a linocut of a jaunty armchair, and this became my logo. I printed 500 cards at the local Kinko's and shuttled them around to local fabric and furniture stores. I introduced myself, showed pictures of slips I'd made and heard over and over again how fantastic it was that someone was finally doing this in Portland. By the end of my first week in operation, I had my first client. Voila! A business was born from a hobby, no need for childcare.

But I got it anyway.

17

WHAT'S SHE DOING HERE?

It was 1994, and Chairwear was in its infancy. I was standing in the kitchen, rifling through the pantry, searching for something to whip into dinner. I'd sewn clear through my intended trip to the grocery store that afternoon and hoped to find something in the larder.

"Let's make dinner!" Mallory called out, as she bounced through the front door with an armful of groceries, my kids, like two little ducklings, behind her. She set a brimming grocery bag down on the kitchen counter. "I got the stuff for your sauce!" she beamed, with that tilt of her head, her lush helmet of hair. She pulled a bottle of wine from the bag, reached into the gadget drawer, and dug out the corkscrew.

This scenario played out over and over during our first year in Portland. I'd grown accustomed to her frequent visits, her offers to help with the kids in the afternoons, often returning them home in time to join in for family suppers.

I had hoped for a night alone with my husband and the kids. Oh well, there was dinner in that bag. She uncorked the bottle, grabbed two wine glasses from the cupboard, filled them both, and handed me one with a clink. I took a quick sip, set the glass on the counter, and unpacked the canned plum tomatoes and fresh basil from the bag. Then I grabbed a head of garlic from the crock on the counter and worked to separate the fat, papered cloves.

"Cheers!" she said with an aw-shucks gush of a smile. "We had a blast, didn't we, kids?"

"Mommy, look what Mallory bought me!" Molly held her new dress to her shoulders as she twirled through the kitchen. Gap tags aflutter.

"Beautiful, Honey. Mallory, thank you, but you've got to stop." She showered my kids with gifts. She never arrived empty-handed. Thanks to her, Molly and Finn could model the entire Baby Gap line from the contents of their closets.

Just then the rumble of Charlie's car quaked the drive. "Daddy's home!" I skipped to open the door and greet my husband.

He grabbed me and kissed me with his usual gusto and glanced over my shoulder at Mallory. She stood in the doorway to our kitchen, all smiles, with a glass of wine in her hand and a hello on her lips.

"What's she doing here?" he whispered in my ear.

"Be nice. She took the kids to the zoo so I could work."

"Again?" I detected a slight irritation in his tone, but the noisy rush of the kids and their happy "Daddy! Daddy!" clatter swallowed it whole. Charlie hoisted Finn to his hip, gave him a big hug and a kiss. "Hey buddy, how was your day?"

"We saw the lions!" Finn, thumb in mouth, slurred with glee. He landed his tattered Lion King cub "Simba," who he called "Bubba," on Charlie's face for a kiss.

Molly held up her new frock for Charlie's approval. "Look what Mallory bought me, Daddy!"

"Nice," a slight wince flitted his face as he tousled Molly's hair.

A babysitter with a bottle of wine and a bag of groceries, what's not to love?

I admit to some ambivalence about her ever-presence. Early on Mallory felt much like a younger sibling—a little sister who was always there, even when you wished she go play with someone her own age. I was grateful for her help with the kids but Charlie's disdain for her frequent intrusions complicated things. Still her presence offered some comfort and gave me someone to commiserate with.

A fierce homesickness had settled in my chest like a bad cold. I couldn't shake it. Mallory was a link to the home I missed—a tonic of sorts. And because we shared a common birthplace, we shared a common vocabulary, a vocabulary of the place we both missed. Los Angeles, with its culture, hip restaurants, beaches, and sun. This shared LA in our DNA created a camaraderie, and over the course of that year, we became friends. Her presence made me feel a little less mournful, a little less alone.

18

THE FRIGIDAIRE FLAIR

That first year in Portland, the white princess phone that hung on the wall in the nook at the back of the kitchen saved me. That princess was my lifeline. My phone-a-friend. Her long curlicue cord stretched clear to the dining room if need be. Hands-free, cradled under my chin, I could check on Finn where he played under the dining table or retract back into the kitchen to keep a watchful eye on what was cooking on the sinister stove. I did it all while confiding in Marina or Ed, even my mother, where they all basked in the California sun.

Marina kept her promise and made frequent visits. In fact, her visits occurred so often that before long, she leased a house at the end of the block, just four doors down on Knott Street. When she was in town, we'd pad up and down the sidewalk in our slippers, weather permitting, under that canopy of trees, carrying cups of coffee in the morning or glasses of sangria at sunset. My Finn and her Timmy, a noisy trike parade out front leading the way. Marina's visits buoyed me. But sooner or later, they'd go back to the sun and leave me marooned in my kitchen tethered to that princess.

We did make friends here in our new home.

Correction: Charlie made friends. I made dinners. Our new friends were all theater people, and they all came through Charlie. This was a change for me. Back in LA, my friends had become his. I felt this group belonged to him. Penny and Josh and Corey and Richard. Josh, the Prop Master at the Portland Opera; his wife Penny, a brilliant set designer; Corey, an actress, and her husband Richard, the tech director at a local theater.

They were great fun and I enjoyed them, but because they came through Charlie, I believed it was Charlie they loved. I was an adjunct. Charlie was the master of ceremonies. I was caterer and set dresser. I strived to gain glory through cooking. In this way, I could hide in the kitchen, and absent myself to my duties. I nursed my growing isolation while serving up platters of grilled flank steaks, filled wooden salad bowls with fresh greens grown in my own garden, tossed in my homemade salad dressing, which Josh dubbed my "secret sauce."

I cooked weekly suppers and brunches on Sundays, and usually something extra in between. I loved to cook, and because we had kids and our new friends didn't yet, our house was the hub. I could tuck the kids into bed to sleep while we socialized.

Despite these weekly gatherings, I was horribly lonely. I felt like an outsider. My real friends, my confidants, were all back in California. I longed for them, like I longed for the sun.

"What's cooking?' Charlie called out over the Sinatra serenade that rang from the speakers in the living room. He sang his way into the kitchen where I stood in front of my nightly nemesis, the Frigidaire Flair.

"You mean what's burning? Damn this stove!"

He wrapped his arms around me from behind, leaned into my backside, raked the nape of my neck with his fingers and planted his lips on my ear, his mouth full of song, "I've got you under my skin..." My knees did a mini dip—that involuntary swoon.

I turned into him, kissed his lips, and swatted him away in one swift movement. "Charlie, we've got to get a new stove. It burned my shallots. Look! This burner won't even light."

"I'll light your burner." He nibbled at my neck.

I fiddled with the knob that corresponded to the large coil on the rear right. A patient pot brimmed with water waited there in hopes to boil. Nothing. Instead, the small burner on the left front glowed bright red.

Back on the day I first toured the house, we trailed our landlady, Marion, her hair a frazzle of wiry gray, into the white galley kitchen. I pointed at the midcentury monstrosity sidled up next to the refrigerator, just opposite the kitchen sink.

"What's that?" I asked.

"It's a Frigidaire Flair," she declared with obvious pride. "Samantha Stephens had one just like it on Bewitched! Look, the oven is on top." She moved her hand, palm up, through the air like an aging spokesmodel, and directed our attention to the chest high double ovens. The glass doors swung up and out like airline storage bins and sported a mid-century squiggle motif. The knobs and dials sat above the oven, gleaming like a space-age cockpit control panel. The whole thing, a lovely shade of root beer brown, sat on a pedestal of metal cabinets, storage for pots and pans.

"Where are the burners?" I asked.

"Wait till you see this!" She yanked at the gleaming chrome

handle—long, lean and pointy—that stretched horizontally below the oven, and with a tug there they were: four burners, hidden in a stainless-steel drawer that, when extended, cantilevered out over the white linoleum floor. This feature would soon prove a nightly hazard for Finn's head.

"Huh," I'd said, disappointed. "Electric."

Cooking, that solitary act, soothed me, enfolded me in a place all my own, a creative endeavor that capped my days. I've always shunned cookbooks. I relished the act of concocting, composing. The night's meal an inspiration born from a craving; a flavor imagined in my head and coaxed from a palette of ingredients into a taste on my tongue. The choosing, the chopping, the sautéed blend of flavors, but even this was fraught. This crazy stove with its faulty wiring robbed me of my daily pleasure.

"What's burning?" Penny called out as she came through the front door.

It was Thursday night on Knott Street. Every Thursday, our friends arrived for must-see TV. We'd potluck a supper, then watch Friends, Seinfeld, and Frasier.

Penny entered the kitchen carting a Pyrex dish of golden peach cobbler; Josh close behind her with a gallon of Tillamook Vanilla Bean ice cream in hand. Penny set the cobbler, still bubbling hot, on the counter. Josh popped the ice cream into the freezer. Corey and Richard arrived right behind them with pre-dinner snacks—a platter of cheese and crusty bread.

"Man, I love that stove, it's so retro." Penny winked at me; a smile lit her dark brown eyes. Penny had the face of a pilgrim. She was a bit of a tomboy, cool yet sincere.

"I think it's kinda cute," Corey chimed, as she gave me a hug, brown curls framing her face.

"She hates it," Charlie laughed as he greeted our guests with big hugs.

"I hate it!" I swirled a fresh batch of shallots in butter. "Josh, can you fix this?"

"Charlie, get your wife a new stove already." Josh leaned in and kissed my cheek. I liked Josh. He was the warm to Penny's cool. His blondish-brown hair, longer than Penny's, was caught in a ponytail that fanned down his back.

Charlie grabbed a couple of beers from the fridge, handed one to Josh and one to Richard and they headed out back to the deck.

"Watch your head!" I hollered at Finn as he toddled into the kitchen. He patted his head at the memory of his last collision and cut a wide path around the "burner-drawer of danger" and headed out back in search of his dad.

19

BREAKING NEWS

"I got it!" Mallory called out as she bounded through the door, a bottle of champagne in hand.

"Got what?" I asked as she popped the cork. It was late spring, and there was sun. It streamed through the kitchen windows and splashed across the floor.

"The internship at the White House!" Mallory explained that a family friend had put in a word for her, and she'd been accepted to the summer internship program.

"Wow, congratulations! What will you do there?" I pulled two glasses from the cupboard. Mallory poured, her glass overflowing onto the counter, champagne bubbling the grout.

"Oh, you know, administration assistant stuff." She grinned and winked.

We kibitzed and giggled, two girls in a kitchen. Mallory's bawdy humor, filled with inuendo, always made me laugh and often made me blush.

"Well, I'll miss you," I said as we drained our glasses.

"Oh, I'll keep in touch," she said, with that tilt of her head and that big beaming smile.

20

WICE GUCKS

At the start of our second year in Portland, Charlie landed a full-time job as technical theater director for a high school in a community near Portland. This rural farm town, home to the Clackamas County Fair with its celebrity pigs and giant pumpkins, was as far from Beverly Hills as it could possibly be. I was grateful for the regular paycheck, but my husband's daily absences stretched into late nights filled with afterschool set building. Soon, his theater rehearsals swallowed our weekends as well.

Mallory had gone off to Washington, and just as promised, she called daily from the White House to check in. She always asked about Charlie and the kids and shared workplace gossip. Her departure meant I lost my one link to LA, not to mention my babysitter. In her absence, I found a new sitter, a high school sophomore named Jane: a sweet shy girl, who'd come to the house each day after school to care for the kids while I worked.

Chairwear was thriving; I sewed up a steady stream of slip-covers and now offered custom-made draperies, as well. Many of the homes I dressed were featured in *Oregon Home Magazine* and the editor soon declared me 'Portland's Queen of Slipcovers.'

"I'd rather be the queen of anything else," I said to Charlie over breakfast one morning. "Your heart perhaps?" He was distracted and distant and irritable. He mapped his work schedule out on the big wall calendar we hung by the stove in the kitchen. His distance ramped up in those days. I worried my homesickness, now a full-blown depression coupled with a general lack of spark, was an irritant to him.

"You won't be seeing much of me in the next eight weeks, the design-build schedule is going to be tight." He put the calendar back on the wall, grabbed his tool belt and headed to the door.

"Who knew being a high school teacher could be so demanding." I followed him through the foyer with a nag of insecurity. "Kiss?"

"Kiss." He planted a deep reassuring kiss on my lips. "I'll be late tonight too. You and the kids should go ahead and eat without me."

"Again?" His sentence settled in my gut like a lead weight. "There's been a lot of that lately," I said, worried I sounded whiny. He shrugged, eyes narrowed as he crossed the porch and climbed into his car.

———

The phone rang from the back of the kitchen. It was Ed, right on cue for our morning check-in. "Hey, it's me. How are you?"

"The rain is killing me. Six straight weeks of it. I might shoot myself." I plunked into my chair at the kitchen table in the nook and spiraled the phone cord around my pinky finger, on and off and on and off, working Charlie's missed dinners through my head.

"You?"

"The smog is killing me. Same old hazy sunshine, day after day."

"Don't taunt me, Edwin. How were your test results?" Truth: AIDS was killing him.

Six years ago, Ed's diagnosis had devastated us both. I was sitting in my office at Robert Graham's studio, when Ed called with the news that he had tested positive for HIV. Bob walked in to find me in tears. Ed had run Bob's foundry a few years back, and Bob was visibly shaken when I shared Ed's diagnosis. "Go down to the boardwalk, Kate. Walk. Breathe. And if you need to, take the rest of the day off."

These days, Ed navigated a daily cocktail of medications and worsening symptoms.

"Better than expected. I just don't feel good." He listed the ailments that plagued him daily, adding a few new ones to the list.

"Sand gucks! Mama! Sand gucks!" Finn toddled into the kitchen.

"Watch your head!" Finn dodged the stove and stood at the French doors that led from the breakfast nook out to the back garden. In the brief summer months, it was the scene of cook-outs and croquet contests, a lush green land. But now, in the dismal November rain, it doubled as a mud pit.

"Sand gucks!" Finn's chubby index finger pointed wildly at the sandbox-turned-wading-pool outside beyond reach. I knew the look in those eyes, blue pools churning. He was about to cross the border into the land of tantrum.

"Ed, can I call you back? Finn's gonna flip."

"Sure, give that kid a hug for me."

"Sand gucks!" Finn clamored at the door.

"Not today, lovey, no more mud."

I'd already done my daily meditation, a hands and knees expedition down the length of the *what-in-the-hell-were-they-thinking* white linoleum floor, that recorded our muddy footprints like an Arthur Murray dance chart.

I love a white kitchen. White cabinets. White counters. But a white linoleum floor? In California or Florida, maybe. But here? Where it rained nine months out of twelve, transforming the solid ground of our short summer to mud, squishy, like a diaper in desperate need of a change.

The real problem, of course, was not the floor, but the pervasive sadness that had seeped into my cells. No amount of floor scrubbing could fix my lonely homesickness. But worse, I had the nagging sense that something was off with Charlie. His absences, so like my father's when I was a kid, buzzed my nerves and reactivated my childhood fear of abandonment. Quite the cocktail when combined with my depression, something I feared I'd inherited from my mother like old heirloom jewelry.

"Sand gucks! Mama! Pease! Mama pease!" I gathered Finn up in my arms, hefted him to my hip and wrestled him into his parka. Out the front door into the rain, I bowed his head into the car and plopped his bottom into his car seat.

I backed out of the driveway, switched the wipers to high and drove the short distance from our house to the local Fred Meyers. That king of grocery stores, like none other. Need lettuce? They had it. A suitcase or snow tires? Coming right up! On this trip, we zigzagged our way aisle by endcap—the distance of three football fields—until we arrived in the housewares department and found the shelves teeming with storage containers.

"Mama? What we do-ing?"

"You'll see, lovey." I seized the longest, lowest plastic bin I could find. Next, we were off to the "Aisle of Rice." I loaded the cart with, "1-2-3-4-5-count'em, Finn!" Five five-pound bags of rice, all white, no brown. "Okay, Finny, now comes the fun part." We made our way to Toyland. I lifted Finn, squealing with joy, up and out of the cart.

"Gucks Mama! Gucks!" It was a grab-and-go extravaganza, as Finn loaded the cart with every earth-moving, dump-trucking, steam-rolling piece of yellow metal that Tonka made, justifiably stretching the budget to maintain my sanity.

Back home, the white linoleum still gleamed from my morning efforts. We sat cross-legged on the floor in the nook, opened all five bags and filled that bin, just shy of the rim, with rice the color of the floor. Finn dug out his new collection of Tonka trucks, all shiny clean and unmolested by the rain and mud outside our back door, and there it began. Just like a new sport debuting at our very own winter Olympics. "Look, Mama! Wice gucks! Wice gucks!"

This was a problem I could solve.

———

A week later, Marina was in town for a visit and over for our morning coffee. We sat in the nook at the back of my kitchen and watched Timmy and Finn as they piloted a yellow armada of Tonka trucks through mountain ranges of white rice. "That's a brilliant thing you made there, Kate," she chuckled.

"Couldn't take those muddy floors one more day."

"Hey, my lease is up at the end of this month," she said. "I need to decide if I'm gonna renew."

"Oh God, please do," I pleaded. "If you don't, I will die here in this mud-pit sinkhole."

———

The next morning, Marina called early. "Get down here. I have news!"

"Come on, Finn, we're going to Timmy's." The two of us headed out the door, on a rare dry day, our slippers scuffing the sidewalk, Finn in Thomas the Tank Engine jammies, me in my white terry robe, cuffs permanently disfigured with coffee stains.

Marina greeted us at the door. She wore a wild ensemble— flowery sleep pants and a big LA Rams football jersey.

"I bought a house!" she squealed before we'd made it through the door.

"You what?"

"I bought a house." She grabbed my cup. "Coffee?"

The house was three blocks east, just north of Knott Street on 39th. Marina described the house in minute detail, explaining she had a little cash from her last screenwriting gig and needed to invest it. "Best part? Immediate occupancy!" She smiled. "I've got the keys! I can move in this week while I'm still in town. Go get dressed. I've hired a sitter and rented a truck. We're going shopping!"

That day, Marina and I went on a thrift store shop-a-thon. Six hours of mayhem and plunder. Two hysterical friends, we laughed uncontrollably, holding our sides, holding our crotches, lest we peed with our laughing. We bought a svelte mid-century red velvet sofa, a dining table, a kitchen table. Assorted chairs, mid-century lamps, all blown glass and barrel shades, a kidney-shaped coffee table, and a pair of 50s bucket chairs that swiveled on brass casters.

We shopped for hours, and at the end of the day, we dragged our haul up the front steps and into her new house. Exhausted and still giggling, we sank, like two drunken sailors, into that flaming red couch.

21

THE HORRIBLE, HIDEOUS, OBVIOUS THANKSGIVING

"Oh, come on, it'll be fun."

"For you, Charlie. I don't know these people. Besides, I've already bought the turkey!" It was Charlie's intention that we spend Thanksgiving at the home of his new boss, Barb, the principal of the high school. I had planned a different day, imagined us hunkered into our big, down sofa. We'd watch the Macy's Thanksgiving Day Parade, then the dog show. A fire crackling in the fireplace, while the smell of roast turkey filled the house. I'd even splurged on a bottle of port. Port and butter, the hallmark of my famous Thanksgiving gravy. The annual tradition: a friendly fight among friends over the remains of my boozy gravy followed by the upending of the gravy boat into the lucky winner's open mouth. All of that would be missing this year.

But worse—the true ache—this would be my first Thanksgiving without Molly. 1995, an odd-numbered year, meant she'd spend this Thanksgiving in Los Angeles with her father.

My homesickness was not helped by Charlie's happy adjustment to our new life in Portland. He loved his new job;

loved the weather, noting it felt more like Wisconsin. There was a growing distance between us, which served to make me feel more isolated, more alone. His long hours at the high school cut into our family time and I worried he was disappointed in me because I was not happy in our new life.

"You can cook the turkey on Friday," Charlie reasoned. "This is important to me." Charlie adored his new boss and his co-workers—one in particular, a young colleague. "She's a great girl. She'll be there with her fiancé and so will Bob, the football coach. I want you to meet them."

We argued about it for days.

"Okay, alright," I finally acquiesced, though I dreaded it.

———

Thanksgiving Day arrived. An epic wind and rain event sent garbage bins, empty from the early holiday pick-up, rumbling down Knott Street with a hollow roar. Lids, like flying saucers, skittered through the air.

Dear-God-this-weather, I grumbled to myself while I stood on our front porch and watched slanting sheets of rain hit the street. "I love you, Mama." Finn, on my hip, snuggled his head on my shoulder; I nosed his hair and breathed him in.

"I love you, too, Finny."

"Come on!" Charlie hollered from the driver's seat, revving the engine.

We dashed through the rain to the car. Drenched, I buckled Finn in, and we were off. The drive south was treacherous. Wet gusts blew across the highway and threatened to lift our car off the road. Charlie and I were silent during the drive. My mood was dark, I could not shake my sulk. A thick stew brewed in my head. Perhaps, I sensed what waited for me there.

Charlie's boss's house, a 1970s-style Brady Bunch affair, was all dark wood, filled with art fair pottery and dusty macramé plant hangers. Spider plants spawned babies; philodendrons choked every corner. Outside, it was black with night, and the wind howled. The dark-sweatered branches of the towering Douglas firs flapped like giant raptor wings, whipping, and menacing the glass.

It started here at this table, right under the cobwebbed chandelier. The moment I saw them together, I knew. No matter that she sat next to her fiancé, his hand clutching hers. She showed off her ring, "May," she said when asked about a date. "We're thinking May." Cheryl was plain, hair in no particular style, skin pale. She smiled wanly at her fiancé, though her attention arrowed toward Charlie. Did anyone else read her body language?

We sat around this table. Barb, the high school principal with her close-cropped gray hair, sat opposite her husband, Bill, clad in red plaid flannel. He carved the bird, knife in hand catching the light from the brass chandelier. Once all were served, I pushed my turkey, dry and inedible, from one side of my plate to the other, and watched.

Over the course of dinner, it was revealed that the ice storm a few weeks back, the one that kept Charlie here in this house overnight had kept Cheryl here too. That news cut deep. I wanted to scream at her milquetoast fiancé. *Don't you see what's going on here?* The inside jokes, the sideways glances. I wanted to yell at our gray-haired hostess. *Don't you see what you've fostered?* But I didn't.

Instead, I folded in on myself. I told myself a story, a tired, old story. My therapist's words echoing in my head. "Kate, you're wrong. It's your fear of intimacy, your insecurity. He loves you. You can trust him."

I battled these thoughts and fears in silence on the long,

dark, wet drive home, with Finn asleep in his car seat. *He wouldn't, couldn't be.* My mind said no, but my body said yes. That fish tail flipped in my gut.

"Isn't Cheryl great?"

"Are you sleeping with her?" I blurted, keeping my eyes trained on the dark wet road. Broken yellow lines ticking past in the headlights, the dash clock blinking 11:11—four exclamation points.

"Kate! She's engaged, for God's sake! And I'm married to you, remember? Look, you're depressed, and now you're imagining things. I'm worried about you."

Watch right here, watch what I did. My husband's ability to lie and deceive was matched by my own to delude. I doubted myself. I denied my intuition—that fishtail flip—now a paddled thrash in my gut. I wrestled that fish and I drowned it. I swallowed his lie. Hook, line, and sinker.

Years later, I would wonder, did I collude? So desperate not to rock our fragile boat—our new life in our new home. Or was it more profound than this? Scripted perhaps. A childhood mandate to repeat and repair? My father's absences, my mother's depression?

Then to his lie, I added my own. I made his lie a truth.

And in this act, I failed myself.

22

THE STOVE BEATER

The rains arrived early our second year in Portland. A wet guillotine shaved our summer short; the unrelenting onslaught stole the end of August. A thick gray porridge bent the sky to the ground.

I struggled to breathe. I yearned for the LA sun, for warmth, for my friends, their faces. I even longed for gridlocked freeways. I would have welcomed a bumper-to-bumper struggle to get to places I knew and wanted to be. Places, like a net of memories that held me; every corner, bus bench, alley, or storefront, all embedded with a remnant of me that told me a story of who I was and where I fit in the world. Everything here was new and unknown. I was lost. Erased in this place.

———

It was early December, and the rain threw daggers at the black rectangles of window that hung over the sink in our kitchen. For all its bright white charm, the kitchen was bathed in gray.

The lamps I'd placed on the counters to spread strategic cheer pitched circles of light from their silken shades, but tonight they couldn't cut the darkness. It was raining in my head now.

Charlie was late. Again.

"Possible freezing rain tonight, folks," the chirpy meteorologist spouted his forecast from the tiny black and white box that sat on the kitchen table in the nook. *Tick, tick, tick.* Icy rain needled the glass. *Tick, tick, tick.* The wall clock echoed. *Late, late, late,* it taunted.

I stood sentry at the Frigidaire Flair. The sinister stove with its haywire circuitry demanded my vigilance. I guarded my sauté. The house filled with the scent of garlic and rosemary as they sizzled in the pot. I tossed in flakes of red pepper, added another glug of olive oil to the hot pan, and checked the burners, wary of their evil dance. It could mean mayhem at any moment.

"Mom, I don't get this!" Molly whined. She sat in the dining room at the big pine table. The light from the chandelier threaded her curls yellow-gold. From where I stood, I could read the frustration on her face, the squinted wince, the darkened glare. Her head tilted towards the open math book; its swoop of pages splayed from its spine. *Damn story problems!*

"Mom! If Tracy paints three paintings on Monday and three on Tuesday...Finn stop it!" Molly brayed and kicked at her little brother. He was under the table in his "fort." He pushed tiny metal cars and trucks on the bright orange Hot Wheels track that he'd woven in and out of a forest of chair legs. He vroom-vroomed, off-roading his mini hook-and-ladder to graze her foot—on purpose.

She kicked.

He wailed.

I guarded the pan.

"Finn, leave Molly alone. Molly, don't kick your brother!"

"Mom, if Tracy paints three paintings on Monday, Tuesday, and Wednesday, and she paints five paintings, eeehhhhhh, I need help!" Her frustration twisted my gut and knotted my shoulders. I might as well have been seven and that homework mine.

"Daddy should be home any minute, Molly. He'll help you." I checked the clock. *Late, late, late.*

I didn't dare leave my post at the stove. I was elbow deep in plum tomatoes. Red pulpy juice streamed my fingers to my forearms. I plucked each juicy orb from the can, stripped the seeds into a bowl, tore each tomato apart and dropped the shred into the pot. I loved this part of making sauce: the tactile satisfaction, my fingers threading each tomato, the sizzle when they hit the pan.

Finn and Molly bickered and kicked. The phone rang. I hovered my hand over the unlit burner at the back of the stove, made sure it was cool and dragged the pot of sauce to safety. I rinsed my hands at the sink, grabbed the dishtowel that hung from the handle on the drawer of burners cantilevered out over the floor, and answered the call. I stretched the cord so I could guard my sauce on the stove.

"I'm going to be late tonight."

"What? You said you'd be home at six. Molly needs help with her homework! Charlie, please."

"Can't. We've hit a snag with the lighting. The kids have agreed to stay late."

"Those kids are more important than your own?"

A hot flush surged my neck and climbed my cheeks. That fishtail flipped. I moved to the back of the kitchen, huddled in front of the French doors, and muffled my plea to shield the kids.

"Charlie, you promised no more late nights. They're forecasting freezing rain; you won't get home at all if you don't leave now." Finn shuffled into the kitchen, his slippered feet scuffing the linoleum. I turned toward his sound.

"Watch your head!" Too late. Finn's head collided with that fucking drawer of danger. The pot bucked on the stove from the force. He rebounded from the impact. His chubby hands flew to his forehead as he fell to the floor. I dropped the receiver; it yo-yoed and hit the wall, dangling from that curly cord.

I dove for Finn and clutched him to me. He sobbed into my neck, all wet and snotty. I pulled his hands from his forehead; a huge purple egg bloomed over his right eye. He wailed in my ear.

"What happened?" Charlie's voice echoed from where it dangled in the receiver. With Finn on my hip, gasping sobs, I fished the phone up from the floor.

"Fucking stove!" I screamed. "Fine! Don't come home!" I slammed the phone into its cradle on the wall.

"Mama! Something's burning!" Molly called.

The acrid smell of smoking garlic and burnt tomatoes found my nose. The piercing cry of the smoke alarm screeched from its spot on the ceiling. Finn threw his hands over his ears and wailed louder, in concert.

"Fuck. Shit. Fucking shit stove!"

"Mom!" Molly scolded, now standing in the doorway to the kitchen.

I planted Finn upright in his slippers on the linoleum floor and silenced the smoke detector with a flip of my dishtowel. I seized the pot from that self-lit burner and threw it in the sink with a smoking clang. I ran the tap, the pan a hiss as water morphed to steam. And then I turned to face my enemy. The Frigidaire Flair—a nightly dare. *Just try to cook*, it sneered.

That's when I saw it, that useless utensil, in the earthenware crock by the stove. The wok skimmer, mate to the wedding gift wok, the one I'd never used. The bamboo handle with its open weave of curved golden wire, a fragile basket meant to lift tender vegetables from the sear of hot oil. I pulled it up and freed it from its spot in the crock. That flat bamboo felt good in my hand, and tonight the wok skimmer found its true purpose. I clutched my weapon—my cudgel, a bludgeon—and attacked my enemy: the stove. I swung and slammed. I bashed and beat. "Fucker!" I screamed and slapped and swore.

Finn scuttled to his sister's side. They stood stock still in the doorway. She held him close like a big sister should and together they witnessed their mother unhinged by fury, grief, sadness, and something else—an unease, deep and unidentified —greater than run-of-the-mill worry. They watched as I unleashed months of angst and ache and loneliness on that Frigidaire Flair. Slam! Whack! Crack! I beat that stove.

When I'd purged myself of all frustration and fury, I slumped to the floor, and I sobbed. Finn and Molly piled on. They cried too, frightened by my rage. A chorus of cries, in a clump on the floor. At last, when we were all cried out, we untangled our legs, arms, and tear-soaked strands of hair and together we let out a collective shuddered sigh.

"I'm sorry, my loves. I'm sorry I scared you. Mommy is just so sad." I rose to my feet, wok skimmer in hand, the wire basket at the end of that bamboo handle now flat as a pancake. As I moved to place it back in the crock, the light from the lamp on the counter silhouetted its weave on the wall.

"Look!" I said, "Mommy made a dream catcher." There on the bulletin board next to the stove where we kept our family gallery of tempera paint and construction paper creations, was the dream catcher Molly had made in school just last week. I held the wok skimmer up next to the dream catcher, and the resemblance was unmistakable. The open weave of golden wire, now flattened, had been transformed by my fury into a catcher of dreams.

23

REACH OUT FOR ME

Darlin' reach out for me
Don't you worry, I'll see you through
You just have to reach out for me
I'll be there, and I'll comfort you...

The next day, my subliminal Dionne Warwick, who regularly inquired if I knew the way to San Jose, offered comfort instead. "Reach out for me...don't you worry, I'll see you through..." She sang this over and over, her voice stuck in my head. I half-heartedly hummed along while I sat in the nook and doodled on my shopping list. The phone rang right on schedule.

"Hey, Katie, it's me."

"Hey, Ed."

"How ya doin?"

"I beat the stove."

"You what?"

I told him the story, the wok skimmer turned stove beater, and ended it with the dream catcher.

"Katie, I'm worried about you."

"It's this fucking rain, Ed, you don't get it. You live in the sun. The rain is killing me. The rain, the stove, they are tied for first place, along with my missing husband."

"Charlie says he's worried about you."

"He called you?"

"Katie, he called because he's concerned, he says you're acting weird, says you're depressed and suspicious."

"Suspicious? Ed, I think he's cheating on me. *There I said it.* I think he is having an affair with his co-worker."

"Charlie told me you'd say that, Katie. You're nuts. He'd never cheat on you. He loves you; he's really worried about you."

Worried I'll find out, I thought, but didn't say.

"Katie, you gotta pull yourself together, you'll drive him away."

"Drive him away? Did he say that?"

"Look, you're depressed, just go to the doctor. Get some antidepressants. Promise me."

"Okay, I promise," I said as I hung up the phone.

Ed knew a lot about antidepressants; his distress over his illness required them. I'd seen how they'd helped him; maybe they would help me too. At this point, I was not only depressed, I was depressed about being depressed. Maybe the doctor would give me a referral to a therapist. I did as I was told and called my doctor.

Next, on the list, I called my landlady. "Marion, this stove is killing me."

"Go to Sears. Deduct it from the rent."

Out the door and off to Sears, I chose a new stove and scheduled the delivery.

I saw the doctor. I told him I was homesick and sad and asked for a referral to a good therapist. "You don't need a therapist," he said, scrawling a prescription on his pad. "Just take these and you'll feel better." *Really?* I'd thought, disgusted by the ease with which the doctor prescribed pills and shunned my request for therapy. I filled the prescription anyway.

The very next day, my new stove was delivered. The boys from Sears delivered me from evil. They carted the Frigidaire Flair off to retro heaven, or wherever it is evil stoves go to die. "Sayonara!" I called out, as they loaded my nemesis into their van and pulled away from the curb. I smiled with relief—a small victory after decisive action.

———

For the next few weeks, I took those damn pills. I gave them a chance. The pills made me drowsy; the pills made me limp; the pills meant no orgasms or clarity of thought. I was muddled and unreachable. If anything, I was *more* depressed. I was submarine.

Dionne still singing *Reach out for me...* I trailed to the stereo, slid her CD into the slot, fast-forwarded to track three, and I listened.

> *When good friends prove untrue*
> *And the things they do to you*
> *They make you feel so bad...*
> *Darling, reach out for me...*

I reached for those pills, ran to the bathroom, and flushed them down the toilet. I stopped them cold turkey—precisely like you're not supposed to. I told no one. I did not tell Ed, and I did not tell Charlie. In the end, I stopped confiding in Ed altogether. He had joined Charlie's team. Best friend turned enemy spy. Our friendship would survive this, but for a time, Ed was lost to me.

At the time, I was deeply hurt by his defection, his allegiance to Charlie. I know now, all these years later, this is what gas-lighters do. They recruit others in their quest to convince you your fears are all in your head—to convince you that their lies are true.

24

FINDING THE SUN

If you were looking for a reason to lose your mind, 1996 in Portland, Oregon, was as good a reason as any. It was the flood year. Even the locals, inured to the rain, could be overheard at check stands and coffee counters saying things like: "Can you believe this? I may shoot myself," followed by incantations containing sun-filled words like Palm Springs, San Diego, and Zihuantanejo.

So, if you hated the rain, the "flood year" would nearly kill you all on its own, no help from extenuating circumstances.

But here are a few:

1. Titration: You have not titrated but gone rogue, cold turkey; the pills you have flushed, you do not miss, but your world has gone sideways. It spins at odd angles. Not all of this is drug induced. Your life is indeed off the rails. Cue: Philip Glass—Koyaanisqatsi.

2. The Wizard of Oz: This, your husband announces, is the spring musical. Your kids will love it. Oh, and by

the way, your husband has taken a cameo role. He will play Uncle Henry opposite Cheryl's Auntie Em. In all the years you've known him, and in all the shows he's done, he has never taken a cameo role. Ever.

3. Fly-Fishing: Your husband has taken up fly-fishing. He buys all the gear. He spends any free time that he could be home with you—his wife and his children— not home, but fly-fishing. Fly-fishing, really? You can think of a hundred puns for this one. All bad. But the one that sticks: Who's that fishin' in your fly?

Which brings us to:

4. Sex: Your sex has not slowed. You are not proud of this given your suspicions but use his hearty appetite to reassure yourself that you are wrong about him, just like he says. He still wants you; he still loves you, see?

5. Chemistry. Something is off in the folds of you. An itch, a burn, a twinge. The smell, not yours, is like a foreign country. The fucker. He fucks her and brings her home to you? So, you ask: "Who are you fucking really? Her, when you fuck me? Or me, when you fuck her?" Crazy, he says. You're crazy. And then he goes fishing. Fly-fishing.

6. Spring break: Your husband announces that he is required to chaperone the high school theater students on the annual spring break trip to Ashland for the Shakespeare Festival. "Required?" you ask, "The whole week?" you say. "Just you? No?"

7. Bombshell: his co-chaperone is the co-worker,
Cheryl. Cue: daggers to the heart.

———

All these years later, I wish I'd been the woman who screamed,
"HELL NO! You're not going to Ashland with your co-worker
and if you do, I won't be here when you get back."

But I wasn't. Maybe he was right. Maybe I was crazy.

Instead, here's what I did:

Molly was required to spend spring break with her father
in Los Angeles. Heartbroken, I drove her to the airport and put
her on a southbound plane. How I longed to fly with her into
the sun, but instead I hugged her and kissed her and asked her
to soak up some sun for me.

"Don't forget the sunscreen," I called to the back of her
head as she rolled her roller bag down the jet way, side by side
with her "Unaccompanied Minor" escort. I stood at the
window and waved at the plane, knowing she couldn't see me,
but just in case she could. I waited until the plane backed out
of the gate and rolled down the runway. "I'll miss you," I whispered to the window as the plane took to the sky.

When I got home from the airport, Charlie was loading
the Suburban with supplies for his stint as a chaperone. Finn
watched from the dining room window as rain pelted the
glass.

He waved at his daddy, thumb in mouth; Bubba, Finn's
beloved stuffed animal, was perma-perched on his shoulder.

"Okay buddy," Charlie said as he came back through the
door. "Daddy's gotta go now." He hefted Finn up, nuzzled his
nose in his son's hair. "I love you, buddy," he whispered as he
covered Finn's neck in tickly kisses. Finn giggled, then wriggled
free and slid down Charlie's leg.

Charlie leaned into me for a kiss. I stiffened and turned. His lips landed off center.

"Have fun," I said as he headed out the door. "Just kidding," I mouthed to the back of his head. I pretended I didn't care, didn't know what he'd get up to with Shakespeare and his co-chaperone. We watched at the window as Charlie backed out of the drive. Finn waved. I didn't.

"Finny, let's go!"

"Where are we go-wing?" Finn slurred.

"We're going to find the sun!"

I gathered our jackets and supplies: juice boxes, cheerios, cheese sticks, apple slices, books, and an old beach blanket, then loaded them into the car. I gathered Finn up in my arms and I loaded him too.

I ran back inside and grabbed the basket of Brio trains and tracks, hefted that afterthought into the trunk and slammed it shut.

I wanted to drive us clear to California. Head home, never come back. But money was tight, not enough cash for that much gas, let alone funds for hotel rooms along the way. And then there was Bella, our ailing blue Volvo sedan. No way she'd have made it.

I'd watched the weather report while sipping coffee that morning and learned that Bend, Oregon, was sunny. I had never been to Bend. I charted our way on a Triple A map with a big yellow highlighter and covered our destination with a huge yellow highlighter sun. We would drive south toward Salem, then east on Highway 22 through the Santiam Pass until we found her. We must find sun.

As we drove, I taught Finn all the sun songs I knew. We sang them one after another. "Here Comes the Sun," "Good Morning, Mr. Sunshine," "The Sun Will Come Out," replacing tomorrow with today-o. When we ran out of sun songs, we sang "Mister Moon," changing the Mister Moon into Mister Sun. Towering Douglas firs, giants on either side of the road, with their long velvety green arms, beckoned to us and then waved at our backs as we drove by. I watched Finn in my rearview mirror as we curved our way through the mountain pass, his cheek pancaked on the window, he looked up at the sky. "Oh, Mister Sun," he called, "come out, we need you, Mr. Sun!"

As we neared Bend, there was promise. We rounded a curve, and I caught a glimpse of blue through a break in the clouds. Clouds white and puffy, not gray, and laden with rain.

"Look, Finn," I pointed out the windshield. "There's blue up ahead."

"Yay! Blue!"

When we pulled into Bend there was sun. "Hallelujah!"

"Hall-ya-uyah," Finn parroted.

We came to a park, luscious and green, wound through by a lazy river. The Deschutes. I rolled Bella to a stop, and we choose a sun-flooded spot near a bend in the stream. I spread the old beach blanket out on the grass. The earth was dry, not soggy, and wet. I pulled out the snacks and the trains, and at last, when all was settled, I stretched out flat on my back in the sun.

And there with the sun on my face, on my limbs, I who had died, was alive again. I cried at the sight of her, the squint of her. The warmth of her hand on my cheek, her fingers in my hair, like a lover, like a mother. *I would live*, I thought. *I will live.*

"Look, Finn, there's your shadow." It had been months since we'd seen our shadows. In a world without sun, all is blotted and blurred. No crisp edges, no clarity, no contrast, a world painted with just one color—gray.

Finn was busy setting up train tracks. I stayed on my back,

felt the sun on my face, soaked her in. "Thank you," I said to the sun, pinned flat while Finn choo-chooed his trains around the track. "Don't move, Mommy, don't move." And I didn't. He'd encircled my body, one wooden bridge spanning my wrist, another my ankle.

Three hours we lolled in that sun. And as I warmed, something in me cracked open. Years ago, in the wake of the rape, I'd lost the God I thought I knew. I'd felt abandoned—thrown from the garden. But here, in this moment, a prayer came. Not to God-the-Father or to Jesus-the-Son but to Mary-the-Mother. It was a woman—a mother—I needed now.

"Mother Mary," I prayed. "Please help." Tears rolled into my ears as I wept flat on my back in the sun. "Mary, Mary, Mother Mary, please help me." The words just came, like an inborn mystery prayer that had lived in me all along. A language learned in another lifetime floated to the surface just when I needed it.

Mary-Mary-Mary. Mother Mary. This prayer, this mother, would save me.

———

Back in the car, I looked at our roadmap and decided to take the long way home. We would go north from Bend, through the Warm Springs Reservation, skirt Mt. Hood and then trace the Columbia River through the Columbia Gorge on I-84.

Off we went, the sun at our backs.

Soon, Finn slept soundly, head tilted to the side, with Bubba as his pillow. While I drove, my prayer continued. It blossomed into a mantra. *Mary-Mary-Mary. Mother Mary— please help.* I repeated this prayer over and over as I drove.

We crossed a vast high-desert expanse, all scruff and scrub pine, and I watched as a dark bank of storm clouds menaced the mountain range to the east. The sky exploded. An epic storm let loose on those distant mountains and painted the horizon with broad rainy brushstrokes. Shards of lightning cracked through the darkened sky; jagged spears stabbed at the mountains below. I felt a shift. Mother Mary? Sun? Storm? *All three.*

In concert with those lightning bolts, I cataloged his missed dinners, countless late nights, weekends swallowed by fly-fishing. He was lying, and I knew it.

When at last I pulled into our driveway, I was determined. I would no longer let his lies separate me from myself. I would learn the truth, and Mother Mary would help me.

25

THE SECRET IN THE SUBURBAN

The proof I wasn't crazy came courtesy of a missing sock.

Another toddler sock gone. I imagined them everywhere: dotting the landscape, charting our movements through the city. Dropped from the height of Finn's shoeless toes while I pushed him in his stroller like a child-king, through parks and parking lots, up and down the tree-lined streets of our gracious, and impossibly green, neighborhood.

The missing sock, mate to Finn's favorite pair, was flocked with little yellow dump trucks. Its disappearance provoked a mini sit-in as I dressed him for preschool that morning. Little arms folded across his chubby chest, feet flailing while I struggled to outfit his pudgy toes with red watermelons instead. "Dump-gucks! I want my dump-gucks!"

Later that morning, Finn at preschool, the hunt for his lost sock forced me out our front door into the—*Dear God, will it ever stop*—driving rain that is early spring in Portland, Oregon. I sprinted the short distance from our colonnaded front porch to the back seat of Charlie's Suburban, that big gray whale of a thing he'd insisted we needed and promptly purchased when we moved up here from California. In a fluke, we'd traded cars that morning.

Drenched, and dripping, down on hands and knees, the torrential rain pounding on the roof like a troupe of Taiko drummers. Aha! The sock!

And then there it was, right next to the sock, the thing I'd been praying for. Proof. Right there under Finn's car seat, along with all those soggy, half-eaten Cheerios.

I ran the distance back to the house, flew through the door, teardrops and raindrops trailing me on hardwoods. I dashed through the living room and into the dining room, sprinted the length of the kitchen and skidded to a stop in the breakfast nook. I grabbed the yellow pages, scanned the Vs, picked up the phone and punched in the numbers.

"Victoria's Secret, may I help you?"

"I hope so," I said, voice catching in my throat. "I've got some tags here, they're from your store. I need to know what they were attached to."

"Pardon me, ma'am, but we're swamped."

"Please, I need to know. Now," I pleaded...and then I lied. "I have a terrible spending problem, I'm in a shopaholic program. Next meeting is today at two. I'm supposed to keep a detailed list of all my purchases, you know, like a food diary for overeaters. Please!?"

I read the SKU numbers into the phone. "OK," she sighed. "Hold on."

I paced the length of the kitchen, into the dining room, and back, tethered by the white curlicue phone cord attached to the wall. I was grateful for the anchor. Weeks of confrontations and his endless denials spooled through my brain and, worse, his constant insistence that I was crazy, paranoid, that it was all in my head.

"Hello, ma'am, are you still there?" The sound of her voice plastered me to the wall.

"Yes, I'm here."

"Lace bustier and matching panties, garters, and thigh-high lace stockings. All red, our Valentine collection."

I slid, the whole broken heap of me, down that wall, puddled on the floor, and wept.

———

Late, as usual, Charlie was barely through the door when I held up the tags.

"I found these under Finn's car seat today."

"What? What's that?" His eyes glazed over with that white-washed innocence of his. "Oh, that? Wardrobe for Oz," he deadpanned.

"Which one?

"Huh?"

"Which one? Is it Auntie Em or the Wicked Witch that has taken to wearing a red bustier and thigh highs?

He stormed past me up the stairs to our bedroom. "Kate, you've really got to get a grip. Your jealousy is out of line and so unattractive."

The next morning, we sat in silence at the big pine table. Rain drummed the roof and windows. Charlie shoveled toast and coffee into his mouth, mute, though I could read the anger simmering in his downcast eyes, his icy distance.

"The kids are excited about the cast party tonight," I said. My plan? To watch the show, study Uncle Henry and his Auntie Em, perhaps catch them backstage. I fantasized an ambush.

"I don't want you there, Kate."

"Oh really." The kids and I always attended dress rehearsals and cast parties. Molly and Finn loved the cast parties best, the rare late-night outing. We'd sit in the audience, watch the show, and cheer the curtain calls. Then we'd all go backstage to join Charlie, the kids in the cast, and the techies—his crew. Cries of "Great show!" joined with high-energy hugs and kisses, and a chorus of happy voices celebrating a great run. Those theater kids all fighting for their turn to carry Finn on their shoulders or hoist Molly up on their hips and parade them both through the set.

"It's too far for you to drive at night in the dark. It will be late; the roads will be wet. It's just too dangerous." He gathered his stuff. "I don't want you there." And with a huff he slammed out the door.

I added his dis-invitation to my PROOF column.

———

In all those dark months of doubt and denial, I'd confided my suspicions regarding my husband's infidelity in two people: Marina, and finally, in Mallory. Mallory, because she called from the White House, every day, sometimes more than once. While at first, I was reluctant to share my suspicions with her, she knew I was depressed, expressed her concern, and quizzed me about Charlie's behavior. Finally, I spilled the secret, relieved to unload my fears on someone who knew him. She was always reassuring, "He'd never cheat on you, Kate, he loves you so much."

Today when she called for her daily update, I told her about the Victoria's Secret tags. She sounded angry at first and then she consoled me as she always did. "I know he loves you, Kate." But today she added, "You know if you do find out he's cheating on you, it may be a blessing, at least you'll know what you're dealing with." *Interesting twist,* I thought as I hung up the phone.

As soon as Mallory rang off, I called Marina.

"Wardrobe for Oz?" she laughed. "Wow-wee! That's rich. Whatcha gonna do?"

"Oh, I've got a plan."

26

THE PAGODA

We met at The Pagoda, a local dive bar that had stood on Broadway since the 1950s. A garish faux "Chinese" affair, it was a ticky-tacky-kitschy place, complete with a little footbridge over a pond filled with half a century's coins: all those hopes and cheap wishes. For what? A better life? A better love? A better marriage? *Perfect setting*, I thought, as we crossed the arched span over the turquoise water into the dark bar. Penny, Corey, and I, settled into a big fan-shaped booth decked out in red metal flake vinyl.

"My treat," I said as we ordered our cocktails, all doubles. My tears hit the wood grained Formica before the waitress had a chance to deliver our drinks.

"Kate, what's wrong?" Penny narrowed her eyes, tilted her head to her shoulder and scooted her cocktail napkin in my direction.

"Yeah, what's going on?" Corey reached for my hand and squeezed it. Her soft brown eyes spouting instant empathy tears. "Oh, Kate, what is it?"

All these months, I'd held my tongue with these two. I

harbored my secret, hoped I was wrong, and desperately tried to believe his lies. But now I was certain, and I wanted, perhaps needed, the support of *our* friends. Penny and Corey adored Charlie. They would be crushed.

"Charlie's having an affair," I declared with confidence. "With his co-worker."

"No way! Not possible!" Incredulous, they shook their heads and rattled off their reasons. "He's so dedicated to you and the kids. Kate, he loves you so much. He's an incredible husband, father, friend." They both confessed they secretly wished their own husbands were more like him.

"No, I'm sure of it." I cited examples of his suspicious behavior, the discovery of the Victoria's Secret tags, the late nights at the high school working on the set. "What parents of high school students let their kids paint sets till two in the morning on a school night?" Then I continued, adding the numerous "sleepovers" at his boss's house because he was too tired to drive the 35 minutes from work to our home. I capped my list with the latest proof, his command just that morning that the kids and I were not to attend the cast party for the Wizard of Oz. Both theater people, I watched their faces register the significance of this.

Still, they could not imagine it.

Clearly shaken by my news, the fact that the two of them believed in Charlie so adamantly, thought him incapable of cheating and of lying, was oddly comforting to me. Their disbelief mirrored my own. He had everyone fooled.

27

CRUMMY CHICKEN

Have I mentioned my husband was good at his job? Set design and lighting were his specialty. He was an expert illusionist. He could make a flat piece of canvas look like an ancient castle. Deftly painted, his faux finishes created centuries-old stones, seemingly rock solid but in truth, paper thin and flimsy.

The Wizard of Oz, his latest production, was no exception. The kids and I had gone to the dress rehearsal and sat in the auditorium. I was dazzled by the set. In the opening scene, the stage boasted an aging farmhouse in the cornfield flats of Kansas that soon transformed into a glittering Emerald City in the land of Oz. Sleight of hand. House of cards. Tornado primed to hit.

Tonight, icy rain and a fierce wind darkened the sky over our house on Knott Street. I trailed through the dining room into the living room and lit all the lamps to fight the gloom. Their silky mismatched shades spilled a warm 40-watt glow on the walls and lit the family photos and vintage landscapes I'd hung in artful clusters throughout our rooms. Back through the dining room, I stopped to adjust the dimmer on the chandelier. Like a radio dial tuned to the right frequency, the correct setting made those golden walls glow deeper. Back in the kitchen, I watched shiny, slippery needles of rain hit the window over the sink. My tired face reflected in the lamplight; those raindrops slid down my cheeks like tears.

"Dinner! I made crummy chicken!" I called from the kitchen to the dining room where Molly and Finn scrambled into their seats. They sat in their chairs like baby birds waiting for me to swoop in with their suppers. Finn's hair glowed like spun gold in the soft light of the chandelier, his red footy pajamas already zipped up under his chubby chin thanks to an early bath. Molly's blond ringlets bounced in the light, the roses of her cheeks, those golden walls, all stolen from a Botticelli. Beautiful babies—mine.

"Yay! Crummy chicken!" they chirped in unison. Finn—my picky eater—was deep into his Creamsicle phase: nothing crossed his lips if not white or the color of Kraft mac and cheese. Molly—my adventurous one—would eat anything. Anchovies, artichokes, even pickled herring. But crummy chicken, white meat cut into strips, dipped in melted butter, and rolled in fresh Parmesan and herby breadcrumbs, then baked golden and bubbly, would make them both happy. I filled their plates with chicken and topped it with extra buttery crumbs scraped from the pan. I added fresh steamed broccoli, hopeful and bright green, drizzled with lemony butter. The scent of lemon and herbs floated through my lamp-lit rooms. I set our plates down on the big pine table and took my seat at the end nearest the kitchen.

Molly had cleared her homework from the table and set it with care, her favorite chore. She'd run out the front door into the driving rain and denuded the pansies that I'd planted on either side of our front walk. She gently toweled them dry and arranged them, their damp, doe-soft, pink-purple faces along with tiny leaves plucked from the hedge out back. She curated all with her innate artistic hand, down the center of those wide pine boards.

"Beautiful job, Molly."

"Where's Daddy?

"Where's Daddy?" Finn echoed. Rain slapped the picture window that looked out onto Knott Street. The still-bare branches of the dogwood tree scratched at the glass. I rose from my chair and drew the draperies against the storm.

"Daddy will be late tonight," I said, taking my seat.

"Again?"

"Again?"

"Finn, stop copying me!"

"Me!"

"Mom! Make him stop!"

"Mom! Stop!" Finn slurred his mimicry, his thumb snug in his mouth, delivering each syllable with a sideways giggle.

"Mom, make him stop!"

"Finn-honey, stop copying your sister." I stifled a grin behind my linen napkin. "And Finny, it's easier to eat if you take your thumb out of your mouth."

"But I want him to see my table." Molly cried.

"I know, lovey girl; we'll leave it just the way you've set it. He'll see it when he gets home."

"Why can't he be here now?"

Why? The simple answer, the cast party for The Wizard of Oz, and the fact we weren't invited, would only make her sadder.

Months of absences. I'd tallied them all on the big family calendar that hung in our kitchen and tracked our comings and goings. Soccer games, play dates, PTA meetings, and potluck suppers. Each month, Charlie and the kids would decorate those dated rectangles with colored pencils. Depending on the month: golden turkeys, big red hearts, green Christmas trees or pink Easter bunnies filled those numbered boxes. This month, the month of March was festooned with a winding yellow brick road trailing its way to a beautifully rendered Emerald City.

My contribution? Tally marks, tiny and black. Nearly unnoticeable in the lower left corner of each numbered rectangle. I tracked all: missed dinners, late nights, overnights, nights he claimed to spend in the guest room at his boss's house due to bad roads, ice storms or exhaustion.

"Daddy's working late tonight," I repeated with a sigh.

Mouths fed, dishes done, stories read, they slept. I dozed there next to Finn, Goodnight Moon askew on my chest. These bedtime naps, so frequent now, were an antidote to my sleepless nights. I roused myself, washed my face, and trailed back into their rooms, kissed their foreheads and tugged their covers up under their chins.

I climbed the stairs to our room, crossed the floor, and turned off all the lamps, save one next to my bedside. I burrowed deep beneath a pile of down comforters, their weight a mandatory ingredient to sleep. But sleep would not come. I knew it.

I read my book; its crispy pages glowed in the lamplight. One paragraph, over and over, the contents of my head overwriting the print on those pages. I watched the clock on my bedside table, the second hand ticked as the minutes dragged me into yet another hour.

I waited.

I waited to hear his car in the drive, the creak of the door as it swung on its hinges. I listened for the clatter of his keys in the dish that sat on the table by the door. I waited.

And then, there it was. The door creaked. The keys clinked. The clock face blinked 2:22.

The muffled plod of his boots on the carpet of the stairs, his guilty creep across the hardwoods to our bed. In the dim light, I saw him lay his tool belt on the chair next to the bed. He held a half-opened package in his other hand.

"Oh, you're still up." He smiled his crooked, lying smile, those crinkled lines around his eyes shone in the lamplight, his golden stubble glowed on his reddened chin and cheeks. Ruddied by cold? By sex?

"What's that?" I watched as he laid the package on our bed.

"A gift," he smiled, "from Cheryl." He unwrapped the package with care and held it up for me to see. "It's an antique barometer...air pressure...tornado...Wizard of Oz. Get it?"

"Oh yeah, I get it."

"Well, since you're still awake," he smiled, turned to grab his hammer, and dug a shiny nail from a pocket in his tool belt. With nail in one hand, hammer in the other; he sunk that silver spike deep into the wall right over his nightstand, right next to our bed.

A tiny action. Concise and clean. Just one strike was all it took, his spiky message loud and clear—he installed her in our bedroom.

"Really, Charlie? You have to hang it there?"

"Yup, I do. It's special."

———

A few weeks later, Charlie had news; he'd been offered a job. Vancouver, Washington, was opening a new high school, an arts magnet with a state of the art performing arts center. They wanted him to help set up the theater department. He accepted their offer and soon he'd handed in his resignation at his current job. He was still insisting his friendship with Cheryl was just that. I knew he was lying, but I took some comfort that he'd chosen this path. At least he wouldn't be with her every day at work.

I had my own announcement. "I've found a marriage counselor," I said. "We start on Thursday." I handed him a slip of paper scrawled with the address.

"Kate, we don't need marriage counseling, you need a shrink."

"Be there," I said.

28

THE BIG REVEAL

It was three o'clock on Thursday, another dark wet day in early spring; our first appointment with the marriage counselor. We sat in silence on opposite sides of the cluttered waiting room, all out-of-date 70s-style—dark wood and new-age tchotchkes. Framed inspirational slogans on the walls stated things like RISE ABOVE THE STORM AND YOU WILL FIND THE SUNSHINE. *Not likely*, I thought.

A door opened and Jim, middle-aged, salt and pepper hair, blue eyes clear behind wire-rimmed glasses, introduced himself and ushered us into his office. Charlie and I sat like lead bookends on either end of the worn plaid sofa.

"Well, let's get started, shall we? Why are you here?" Jim smiled, sincere. "Charlie, why don't you go first?" Charlie sighed, took a deep breath, and launched into a list.

"She's depressed, she's anxious, and she's suspicious. She hasn't adjusted to our life in Portland." I nodded. *All true.* And then: "I think maybe she should go back to LA—take an extended trip," he said. *News to me*, I thought.

I shrank and twisted in on myself. Charlie's voice droned.

My heart constricted. Jim leaned in and handed me a box of Kleenex. "And Kate?"

I struggled to speak. My voice wet, sticky, cracking, fists full of soggy tissues. And then I unspooled it. The late nights, the Victoria's Secret tags, the hang-ups, those countless clicks on the phone line whenever *I* answered. His mistress, I presumed. Then I reeled it all the way back to Opera Girl. "You cheated on her with me, remember? Was I her LA Girl? And what about Robe Girl? Did you sleep with her too?"

Charlie shook his head, and his eyes did the thing they do; a windshield wiper whitewash, wide-eyed—a feigned innocence.

"He's having an affair. I know it. He won't admit it, he just tells me I'm crazy."

"Kate!" Charlie flared with faked outrage. "Your jealousy is unwarranted and so unbecoming."

Without missing a beat, Jim turned to Charlie. "Are you?" Silence. "Charlie, are you having an affair?"

I liked this man.

"Charlie, I'll ask you again." I inhaled and waited; a small knot of tension uncoiled in me.

Charlie sat in defiant silence; arms folded tightly across his chest. The petulant man-child I knew so well. And then, a mumble, a murmur. "I wouldn't call it that."

"What would you call it then?" Jim asked. No answer. "Charlie, what would you call it?"

It went on like this. By the end of that excruciating 50-minute hour, my husband had admitted to a "close friendship" with Cheryl, his co-worker. "That's all it is," he said repeatedly.

———

Next morning, kids at school, I was sitting at the kitchen table. I watched the wind and rain as it trampled the unmown grass, forced my rose canes to the ground, and threatened to break limbs from the towering walnut tree. The kids' swing that hung from a branch some thirty feet up, ridden by a ghost child, whipped through the air like a carnival tilt-o-whirl.

I wouldn't call it that. I wouldn't call it that. The phone rang and bumped the needle stuck in my brain. I lifted the receiver and dragged it back to my chair.

"So? How'd it go?" Marina's voice chimed in my ear.

"The counselor asked him flat out if he was having an affair."

"And?"

"He said he wouldn't call it that, the fucker."

"What would he call it then?"

"Hang on, Marina, there's another call coming through." I hit call waiting, "Hello? Kate? This is Cheryl." Her voice was halting and brittle. "Look, I know you two are trying to work things out, but Charlie's not telling you the truth. Can we talk?"

I stifled a gasp and steadied myself. "Yes, let's talk." We made a plan and I clicked back to Marina.

"Oh my God, Marina, it was Cheryl."

"What? What does she want?"

"To talk."

"Good, and remember the less you say, the more she'll tell you."

———

I paced the floor. I lit a fire and paced some more. And then a knock. I opened the door to let her in. Cheryl, my husband's lover, was the definition of plain, dressed in nondescript clothing, the color of the rain, mousy brown hair in bad need of a good cut. Young, early twenties. I sat her strategically in a chair opposite the wall of our beautifully framed family photos—husband, wife, and two beautiful children.

I followed Marina's instructions and let her do most of the talking. Her story sucked the air out of my lungs. "It's just what married men do," he'd told her. "He said he loves me, needs me, can't live without me." She went on. He'd urged her to break up with her fiancé. Promised his undying love.

As she spoke, months of dark doubt, those thick rainclouds that had settled in my head, cleared. Click, click, click. Autofocus. All the jagged puzzle pieces, his absences, his gaslit lies, Mallory's daily calls from Washington, her uptick in anger when I told her about the Victoria's Secret tags, all assembled into a clarified picture, long fuzzy, now clear as cut crystal.

Strangely calm, when I'd heard enough, I spoke. "I suspect you're here not out of concern, but out of hope to bring a quick end to my marriage. However, if you're planning on a long and happy life with my husband, I think you should know, I don't think you're his only 'other woman.'" I took an airless breath and listed a few I now saw as real possibilities, and at the end of a long list of friends and co-workers, I paused and considered. "And then, of course, there's Mallory."

Her face went dark, "Mallory? I hate Mallory!"

"You know Mallory?"

"Well, I don't *know* her, know her." She explained that Mallory had left her a voicemail at work. "It was meant for Charlie, but she left it in my mailbox by mistake."

"Some mistake," I said.

The gist of Mallory's message: she was coming to Portland, and she "couldn't wait to see him, couldn't wait to..." You get the idea.

That did it. I stood up, grabbed my keys and coat, and pushed Cheryl toward the door.

"Where are you going?" she asked.

"To see to my husband."

"But-but-but," she stammered, eyes full of alarm. "It's my birthday today! He's taking me to lunch!"

"Wow! Well, I guess you'll just have to find somebody else's husband to have lunch with today."

———

Spinning, no place to stand, gravity had abandoned me. I was circling the earth at the speed of light. No foothold possible. I looked back. I looked down. Everything—my children, my home, all of it—flew to bits and entered earth's atmosphere, in chaotic orbit.

I wouldn't call it that! You fucker!

I flew out the door. Bella, a fiery chariot on autopilot, somehow transported me from our house on Knott Street across the Columbia River that divides Oregon from Washington, to the school where Charlie now worked. I was Judah-Ben-Hur, shimmering white stallions at full gallop out in front of me. Their manes, my hair, a fiery blaze streaking the sky. Everything made sense now.

I parked the car with a screech and ran through the rain, toward the school's main entrance. I crashed through the massive double-doors and sent them flying—weightless, like playing cards. The school receptionist jumped from her chair. "Ma'am, you'll need to sign in!" Ignoring her, I barreled down the corridor toward my husband's office and barged in like a battering ram.

There he was. He sat leaning back in his chair, feet up on his desk, joking with his co-worker, his new best friend. He was a sweet guy, a born-again Christian who thought Charlie could do no wrong.

"What's up? What's wrong?" Charlie stammered; eyes wide.

"I've just had a visit from your mistress."

"Who? What? What are you talking about?"

"You know, the girl you've been fucking? She just left our house." I shouted it loud, not caring who heard.

Stricken, he glanced in the direction of his friend, still sitting across from him, mouth agape, taking it all in.

Charlie whisper-shouted, "Kate, keep it down!"

I yanked him by his shirtsleeve, up and out of his chair. I dragged him to the door of his office and down the hall, not caring who saw. We spilled out the door and into the parking lot in the direction of the Suburban. He hopped in behind the wheel as I opened the passenger door. In a flash, I saw it. His beloved fly rod.

"Fly-fishing, you fucker!" I grabbed that rod in its titanium tube, and in my hands, it became a billy club. I swung, and I swung hard, crafting a chain of dents, perfectly spaced, and artfully executed, all the way down the side of his beloved Suburban.

"Not my pole!"

"Oh, that's rich, Charlie!"

I climbed up into the Suburban and slammed the door as he sped out of the school parking lot. He rolled to a stop on a little side street and parked the car in a neighborhood of tidy clapboard cottages, all barely visible through the torrential rain.

"It's just what married men do? Really? You fucker!"

"I'm sorry, Kate!" he cried, eyes trained straight ahead at some invisible point on the blurry horizon.

"I want the truth, Charlie! All of it!"

"I'll tell you everything. I promise!"

I fired my questions like bullets. Why? How could you? For how long?

He sobbed through his answers, admitting to all that Cheryl had told me. And then, when I'd heard all I cared to about Cheryl, I moved on.

"Now, tell me about Mallory."

"Mallory? What about her?"

"Don't lie, Charlie! I know."

It seemed like hours we sat there in that cold dark rain. Thick condensation formed on the windows as chilled air mixed with hot breath and a torrent of tears.

Our life—my life—imploded with each sentence spoken.

Yes, Mallory.

Yes, for years.

And yes.

Even before we were married.

29

THE BAROMETER WAS THE FIRST
TO FLY

I don't recall the turn of the key or the roar of the engine or the drive back home. I don't recall my clench of the wheel or my foot on the gas, though it was my foot, my furious foot, that pounded the pedal and fueled my careen over rivers and bridges. The road signs smeared useless by tears, rage, and speed. I don't recall the screech of the brakes or the whip-flex of my neck as I slammed into our drive.

But I do recall a frantic need. To break. To smash. To burn.

I do recall my charge to the door, the key in the lock, the door's crash to the wall. I do recall my rush up the stairs, my feet on the treads as they flew two by two.

Yes, I do remember the flight to his bedside, my lunge at that relic. That antique barometer she'd given to him. Now a gift to me.

I do remember the heave of that window, the crash of the sash weights as they blasted their bounds. I do recall the hurl, the pitch, the plunge, the drop. I sent that barometer straight to the ground and I watched it explode like a bomb on our drive. That gift from her, his precious antique, its secret significance now transformed by my alchemist's action into bits of wood and shards of glass and crumpled metal, like shrapnel sprayed from the barrel of a gun. That transmutation of what was whole, now splayed and shattered. Just like me.

The barometer was the first to fly.

That explosion on the driveway, so deeply satisfying, was a gateway drug that now had me in its grip. I raced down the stairs, threw open our cupboards and raided our cabinets and counters and shelves. I ran those breakables out to the yard and hurled them, one by one, at the side of our garage. My fury, the ache, his lies, the hurt—all hit that wall and crashed to earth.

"Mommy, what are you doing? Mommy! Mom!" Molly's voice filtered through my rage. She stood on the grass flattened by the cold spring rain. Her cherubic face half hidden in the hood of her purple raincoat. She called to me from the other side of the weathered picket fence that separated our yard from the vegetable garden.

"Oh, Honey, you're home." I don't know how long she'd stood there, lunchbox in hand, knee socks askew. How many plates she saw fly from my fingers like fastballs. How long she watched as they hit the side of the garage and shattered, that spicy splintering sound, the satisfying smash that sent shards flying.

"Mommy! What are you doing?"

"Here, pick one. Try it. You'll like it." I pointed to the pile of dishes that sat in the mud just inside the garden gate.

"But, Momma, why?"

"Because it feels good. Try it."

She set her lunch box down in the wet grass, entered the garden and knelt to the stack. She pulled an old floral butter dish out of the pile and looked to me for permission. With a nod of my head and an encouraging smile, I welcomed her into my private club.

"Go ahead," I coaxed. She cocked her arm, checked my face again, and then she let that dish fly. It shattered and all those tiny bits and slivers joined with mine and settled in the fertile earth of our garden. My vegetable patch where I'd tended lettuce and arugula, basil, and tomatoes—my life-giving garden, now a killing field.

"Wow!" she said. "I see what you mean!" Molly lifted another dish from the pile and cocked her arm. "I hate you, Brandon!" she cried. Brandon, the class bully, her daily scourge.

"That's right!" I called, as she took aim again and sent that saucer to meet its end.

———

Mallory called later that afternoon. "God, Kate, I'm so sorry," she cried into the phone.

"I see you've spoken with my husband."

"Kate, I'm sorry, I care about you—you're my friend."

"My friend? Some friend, Mallory!" I yelled slamming the phone into its cradle. I now understood all the months she had called me from Washington; her long hours of "friendship" were all an attempt to stage-manage, to use me—my confidences—to keep tabs on her lover, my husband. Another betrayal. I was galled by her duplicity, my husband's lies, and their collusion to deceive me—a double whammy of gaslighting.

———

As soon as Charlie arrived home that night, the kids asleep in their beds, I launched my assault. "Why? Why were you so desperate to marry me? What a con! Ten times you asked. Ten times you proposed! Was it all just pretend? Stage dressing? One of your beautifully rendered falsehoods, a carefully crafted folly to hide behind. Family man?"

"Kate, I love you. Please! I need you."

"Did we move to Portland so you could fuck Mallory? Tell me! Did I give up my life, my career, so you could fuck her?"

"She had her pick of colleges! She chose Lewis and Clark because she knew we were planning to move here. I tried to end it, but she threatened to tell you. I was scared."

"Oh, poor you, Charlie!"

All these years later, I still don't know which came first, Charlie's push to leave LA and relocate us to Portland, or Mallory's choice to attend college here.

———

The next day I dragged Charlie back to our marriage counselor; a painful pilgrimage to Jim's brown-plaid couch.

"Not just one mistress, he has two. I get a BOGO! He slept with a student!" I cried.

"She wasn't *my* student." Charlie explained that she was attending Santa Monica College when their affair started. "She was nineteen!" he cried.

I recapped the events of the previous day to Jim and then I launched in.

"Have you fucked them in our bed?"

"Kate!" Charlie cried, the wounded victim.

"Oh what, that question hurts you? I've hurt your feelings? Did you bring them to our house and fuck them in our bed?"

"You need to answer her," Jim instructed.

"Yes," he mumbled.

"Which one?"

"Cheryl."

"When?"

"When you went to LA to see your grandmother."

"You fucked her in our bed while I was visiting my grand-mother as she lay dying in the hospital? Nice Charlie. And where were our kids?"

"Asleep."

"Where else?"

"What?"

"Where else? On our couch? In our basement? On our guest bed?"

"Yes. Yes. Yes."

I should have ended it all right then.

But I didn't.

30

MONOGAMY

mo nog a my

mə'näɡəmē/
noun: monogamy

1. The practice or state of being married to one person at a time.
2. The practice or state of having a sexual relationship with only one partner.

"**D**id you even consider it?" I glared at Charlie from my seat at the big pine table next morning.

"What?"

"Monogamy." I understood for the first time, and way too late, this might have been an excellent question to ask my intended when considering marriage. Silly, stupid me, somehow while my gut whispered I could not trust him, I did believe his public "I DO" implied I was and would forever be his one and only.

The reality that Charlie's affair with Mallory was already in play on the day we wed was devastating. Waves of nausea sloshed me—so stunned the man I loved turned out to be the man I'd feared him to be. Why had I ignored my intuition? Because I hoped he was 'The One?' Because I hoped that this man, this relationship, was my salvation?

Fairytales I told myself.

All these years later, I wonder: Did I fail to ask the question because I didn't want the answer?

31

THURSDAYS WITH FRIENDS

A knock at the door and in they came. It was a Thursday night and Penny and Josh, and Corey and Richard, arrived on Knott Street en masse, for the formal inquisition. Our Thursday frivolity had turned funereal—no wake, no potluck, just a public flogging. We set the time for later than usual, the kids sound asleep in their beds. We sat ring around the roses, a somber group in the lamp-lit living room. No Must-See TV this Thursday—just ashes.

We all fell down.

Each soul took a turn at bat. With tears in his eyes Josh went first. "What the fuck, Charlie, what were you thinking? I looked up to you. I'm heartbroken for Kate, but also for us. I thought I knew who you were, but I don't."

Richard was up next. He sat on the couch, in his flannel shirt and blue jeans, hunched over as if in physical pain. "Charlie, I feel so cheated. I modeled my role as a father on your example."

Corey dabbed at the corner of her eyes with a tissue. "Charlie, how could you? I am heartbroken, shocked. So disappointed in you. How could you do this to Kate? To Molly and Finn?"

Charlie sat, shrinking in the big wing chair cornered by the fire. He sobbed. "I'm sorry. I will make it up to you, to Kate and the kids. I'm sick," he said. "I need help."

"I'll say," Penny, known for being blunt, pulled no punches. "Listen, you need to get help, I love ya, buddy, and I'll support you to get well as long as the lying and the cheating stop now."

"So, Charlie? What's your plan?" Josh asked when Penny was done.

Charlie did not try to defend himself. He promised to change. "Please give me a chance to prove myself to you. Please stand by me," he sobbed. "I will go to therapy with Kate. I will get better."

I sat mute, shell-shocked, and spent, and for the moment, all cried out. I watched as *our* friends championed *my* cause. I'd always felt they were Charlie's friends, but in that moment, I could see their fierce loyalty to me, and my heart brimmed with gratitude.

Josh rose from his seat across the room, walked over, and squeezed my shoulders, "Kate, we are all here for you, we will support you in whatever you decide."

32

THE PROMISE RING

Devastated that something I knew I knew—but was so desperate not to know—could break me so completely. I sat in the living room, glued to my chair. Scenes from our life looped through my brain like an old home movie. Brittle super-eight ticking through a tinny projector, revealing the life I had built was a fantasy with a shocking plot twist. I was stunned by the enormity of Charlie's betrayal. Not a one-night stand; not a brief fling; not just one mistress, but two. Two that I knew about. All those years of intimacies, years of lovemaking, years of birthdays, anniversaries, dinner parties—seven years of marriage undone by seven years of lies.

Charlie arrived home early. He came through the door carrying a shopping bag, took a seat in the wing chair, and reached to turn on the floor lamp. "Why are you sitting in the dark?" he asked. I hadn't noticed. "We'll get through this," he added, with a pleading edge to his voice. He sank down into the wing chair, called the kids into the living room, sat them at his knee, and reached into the bag like a department store Santa.

"Finn, honey, Daddy bought this for you." Finn's eyes

gleamed as he wrested a soccer ball from his father's hands. Charlie had promised to teach him to play months ago. Finn set the ball down and started kicking it around the living room.

"Finn," he said sternly, "what do you say?"

"Tank ew, Daddy,"

"And Molly, this is for you." He handed Molly a My Little Pony, a toy she'd retired a year ago. Molly's face darkened. "But Daddy...I don't..."

"Molly?"

"Thank you." Molly set the purple pony down on the coffee table.

"Now give me a hug and go play. I need to talk to your mother." Finn gave Charlie's knees a hug and kicked the ball towards his room. "Hug?" He looked to Molly, who complied and then trailed off to her room, leaving the pony behind.

Charlie shifted in his chair, took a deep breath, and tugged a little black box from his coat pocket. He held it out to me, where I sat plastered in my chair opposite his own. He balanced the box in his upturned palm; his fingers splayed flat like a platter.

I'll admit the sight of that velvet box gave me a thrill. We bought my wedding ring at a California flea market, a place-holder for the "real ring" Charlie had promised all those years ago.

"Kate, this ring signifies my intent to be a better man, a better husband, and a better father," Charlie proclaimed, as I opened the little black box. My heart fell when I saw it. The diamond chip, so minuscule, required a microscope to find it where it sat atop a decidedly unlovely setting.

"Do you like it?" He took my hand and worked the skinny band onto my finger, the edges so sharp they threatened to cut into my skin. I nodded yes, thinking *no*. In that moment, my heart so broken, no diamond would have mended it. But this ring, so insignificant, so meager, struck me as woefully wrong, like applying a Band-Aid to a gaping wound that required a trip to the ER.

Still, I'd worn it anyway, a hopeful gesture. I hoped I could believe him, hoped our marriage could withstand his lies and my rage at his betrayal.

And I hoped his promise carried more weight than that stone.

33

MIRACLE ON 39TH STREET

I t was my foot that rocked the bed. Though I couldn't tell you which came first, the clench in my chest, my heart in my throat, or the rubber band relay that played down my leg. But it was my foot that would not quit. In the days and weeks that followed the big reveal, I woke to this quake, the rock of the bed, and the creak of the springs that came with it. Fear shouting in my ears: How will we live? Where will we live, my children and I?

Each day I woke to this fear and my Mary mantra was there in my heart, in my head, on my breath. Mary-Mary-Mary. I prayed my one-word mantra as I swung my worried feet to the floor, threaded my legs into sweats, shoveled my feet into socks and shoes and padded down the stairs. Charlie sleeping soundly as if blameless.

It was four in the morning, but no matter. I donned my coat, my hat, my gloves and I'd go out into the still dark morning. Rain or not, ice or not, I left the sleeping house and walked my one-word mantra. Mary-Mary-Mary-Mary.

I walked, and I walked fast, propelled by a deep inner

panic, up through the neighborhood onto the ridge above my house. Stately homes stood sentry. I imagined them all, containers of happy families and faithful husbands. Lights flipped on, coffee perked, newspapers unfurled, husbands greeted wives with good morning kisses, lunches were made, followed by breakfasts.

Left-right-left-Mary-Mary-Mother-Mary. The physicality of my footfalls and my Mary mantra were the only anecdotes I'd found to calm myself: all frayed nerves, broken heart, and shattered life. I walked, and I walked faster, until I'd walked the anxiety into exhaustion, and then I made my morning pilgrimage to the house on 39th Street.

It was a miracle this place existed, Marina's house, the little house on 39th, just a few blocks from my own on Knott Street. Built in 1924, it was a cream-colored clapboard with multi-paned windows across the front and had a wide wooden porch framed by giant blue hydrangeas, flowering or fading, depending on the season. Over the years, Marina's visits had slowed, and when she wasn't in town, I was its caretaker, and it was mine. This place became my refuge.

The key in my coat pocket, I'd let myself in through the back door that opened into the tiny kitchen. I'd switch on the hobnail lamp atop the old kitchen table, a dim 40 watts spilling a warm glow across the red-speckled linoleum floor. I filled the dented copper kettle, lit the flame on the old O'Keeffe and Merritt, and made myself a cup of tea. Then I'd open the little door to the kitchen pantry and there at the back, steep and hidden, I climbed the secret stairs to my sanctuary in the attic.

My sanctuary? A place of my own at the top of the stairs awaited me in the dormer. An old twin mattress piled high with down comforters and velvet pillows, pilfered from my own linen closet. My altar? An old leather suitcase set on its side and draped with a silk scarf. Candles and incense and sage at the ready, I'd light them all, my altar-top Mother Mary glowing in the candlelight. Ready to assist, were my spiritual advisors— a stack of books, Rumi and Hafiz, along with my tarot cards, box of runes, and the I-Ching.

I would sit and read and write and pray and cry and sometimes exhausted, curl up and fall asleep, all before 7:00 am. Then I'd drag myself back down the stairs, turn out the light, lock the door. I'd walk back to my house on Knott Street just in time to wake the kids, hug them tight, make their breakfast, and get them ready for school.

If Charlie knew of my morning escapes, he never acknowledged them. If I was lucky, he was dressed and ready to go to work when I returned. Really lucky? He'd fly out the door as soon as I got home.

34

A HOLEY BOAT

Anger sinks the boat.
—Hafiz

As a child I learned, courtesy of my mother's psychiatrist, that depression was anger turned inward. Armed with the truth and a reason for mine, I externalized it. I marinated, waded in deep and pledged to feel it all. Anger. Rage. Sorrow. I would not turn away from it, I would not push it down, I would not let it fester and riddle me like a cancer.

I filled my days with little rituals, and I allowed them all. What I couldn't break, I'd burn. One day I dragged the old, galvanized washtub out of the garage and christened it—a fire bowl. I spent hours on scavenger hunts going through Charlie's drawers and closets. I unearthed hidden love notes from his other women written on scraps of paper or scrawled in the margins of old theatre scripts. There were cards from Mallory in Washington and notes from Cheryl. I'd sit on the little wooden campstool out in the driveway and toss each trespass into the flames. I watched the flare devour the evidence—the proof of his misdeeds. I felt a need to destroy him.

In the early days of this devastation, I worked to keep our boat afloat. I wanted to believe Charlie could change. I attended our weekly therapy sessions. He claimed he'd never cheat again, swore those other women meant nothing to him. But nothing he said rang true. He had proven himself a colossal liar—an incredible con. How in the wake of his lies, could I believe anything he said?

I banished Charlie to the couch, but he'd turn up in our bed, halfway through the night, like a needy toddler. He was home most evenings now. He helped with the dishes and read to the kids and mowed the lawn, like husbands are supposed to do. He professed his love and begged me to forgive him. Me? I loved this man, and I hated him too.

Cheryl still called and hung up when I answered.

Anxiety coupled with paralyzing fear threaded my days. I was a yo-yo of should I stay, or should I go? Grief over another failed marriage, and incessant worry over my ability to support the kids on my own, rattled my brain. How would this affect my children? Molly had already lost one father; if I ended this marriage, she'd lose two. And what of Finn? What would this do to him? Could I even be a single mother to two?

I did not discount my responsibility for this mess; I was full of self-recrimination. I chose this boat, this unworthy vessel. I'd loaded my children and myself into a hull shot through with holes. I had ignored that whispered warning of intuition, that tiny unformed part of me that knew, that *really* knew, but didn't know enough to listen. I would listen now.

Hafiz says anger sinks the boat. What of infidelity?

———

My 40th birthday arrived. Before the big reveal, Charlie and I had planned to spend the weekend together at the beach. At the last minute, he begged off, claiming an obligation at work. I was hurt but relieved, the thought of spending time alone with him was repugnant.

I drove to the coast and rented a room with a view across the road to the waves. I spent the day on the beach, eyes filled with ocean, fingers sifting handfuls of sand, tears caught in strands of my hair as it blew about in the wind. When the sun dropped into the sea and the mid-May chill chased me back to my room, I sat on the bed and assessed my situation.

Raped at 30, divorced at 31, now 40 and betrayed. No self-pity, just an honest appraisal followed by a profound need to understand why. Why had I made the choices I'd made, and what was I meant to learn?

When I was in college, I learned my father had had an affair. My mother never knew. His longtime paramour was a family friend. I understand now, we arrive in young adulthood drawn to relationships modeled for us in childhood. We choose what feels familiar.

All these years later, I see it so clearly. I married my mother in Hank. His constant belittling mirrored hers, and felt like home to me. In Charlie, I'd married my father, a man capable of deception—this was also my home.

Not long after the rape, a counselor said something to me that stuck. "Think of life as a pie, Kate. Some slices are bitter, others sweet. All are required to make up the whole. In the end, there will be balance."

This decade, I had baked the bitter bits. There must be sweet slices in my future.

I lifted the hotel bible from the drawer in the nightstand next to the bed and it fell open to this: "Lo, though I walk through the valley of the shadow of death, I will fear no evil."

And I knew Charlie was with Cheryl.

35

THE PROMISE PRISON

Looking back, what surprises me most is that I stayed so long. I knew myself to be someone determined to make things right even when blatantly wrong, often staying way past the expiration date. I was a Taurus, after all. I was in shock and paralyzed by fear—both financial and logistical.

But more than this, I understood, I'd built myself a promise prison on the day I said, "I do." I bricked those walls sky high, mixed the mortar strong. The vow I'd made, for better or worse had turned the lock and tossed the key. The other vow, the one I'd made to myself: Two marriages okay, two divorces—no way —this was a deadbolt.

I was unable to see a clear path forward. I needed a plan. Practical and pragmatic, I would take my time. Charlie had been cheating on me for at least eight years—eight I knew about. I figured I was justified in taking as long as I needed to figure out what I was going to do, and how I was going to do it.

In the end, I needed help to undo my "I do," so I enlisted a team. I found my own therapist. I consulted a psychic. I hired tarot readers, a shaman, and an astrologer. I paid them in trade, bartering for their services with slipcovers and pillows and cushions. They were a team of seers who lent me their tools and taught me how to use them.

36

RUMI AND THE CHRISTMAS CARD

It had been six months since the big reveal and the trees on Knott Street were shedding their leaves. Today, as November dragged on towards December, I watched the leaves drop one by one, and imagined each leaf a tear.

I sat at our big pine table, old long before I'd bought it off the back of a rusty blue truck at the monthly antique market in our neighborhood back in California. The burly guy with his winking eye that drove up from Mexico every third Sunday to sell his wares had promised to bring me a great table, and he did. That long-ago Sunday, he'd offered his hand, rough and calloused, and helped me up into the back of his truck. "I waited for you. You get first pick."

Out of the four or five tables that made the trip across the border that day, I chose this one, seven-feet-long by four-feet-wide. Perfect. Five wide planks, warm and smooth, the color of burnished gold, sat squarely on a pine apron supported by chunky hand-turned legs. Those four legs had a bit of a wobble, and sometimes a squeak. No matter, this table had character. Rich with a patinaed history long before it joined our family, we'd added our own. I imagined it recording each event in its fine layer of scratches and stains left by family art projects, tearful math problems, spilt milk and sangria, sloppy Saturday morning pancake breakfasts and boisterous dinner parties. All played out here.

Today my table served as my desk. I sat and addressed my handmade Christmas cards, distracted by the dervish dance of leaves in the wind and rain just outside my dining room window. My old leather address book, tattered and worn, lay open on the tabletop. Like an almanac of marriage and divorce, success and failure, each soul's life traced in a series of street names and cities, blacked out, crossed through, and amended.

The front door swung open and in he came from wherever it was that he went. "Fly-fishing," he said. I didn't believe him. He was wearing the corduroy coat I gave him last year for Christmas. It was the color of toasted caramels, the same color as his hair. Lined in cornflower blue flannel, the same color as his eyes, it made them bluer than the bluest blue. I remember how handsome I thought he looked in it, that Christmas morning, all scruff and tousle. "I love it!" he'd said, with a deep kiss and a hug.

Where had that handsome husband gone? Had he ever existed? In that moment, all I knew was that love, ardent and passionate, had morphed. I hated him now; hated those lying eyes, that aquiline nose, his cheating lips, those honor scout ways.

All of it.

"Hey," he said as he shuffled across the hardwoods, his boots tracking rain through the dining room on his way to the kitchen.

"Hey. Listen, I've canceled the White Elephant this year," I said, as I licked another envelope and pressed it closed.

"What? Why?" He glared at me from the doorway that led to the kitchen.

"I can't pretend, Charlie."

"Kate, when are you going to stop punishing me? What about Penny and Josh? Corey and Richard? The kids? They'll be disappointed."

I was disappointed too. The White Elephant, our annual Christmas party, was our biggest bash of the year. A raucous gift exchange. Friends came through our door carting kooky gifts. Laughter filled our cozy living room as presents were opened and changed hands, traded up or traded down. We'd potluck a big yummy meal, my old pine table heaving with deliciousness. I'd miss this party. But it was broken. Everything was broken. Just like the plates I threw at the side of the garage.

"I've already told Penny and Corey. They're disappointed, but they understand." The truth was they couldn't and didn't want to pretend either. Our entire extended family was suffering in the wake of Charlie's betrayal.

———

On a rare sunny day in early December, I strapped Finn into his stroller and set out for the local mailbox. My handmade Christmas cards were tucked in at Finn's side. He was bundled up in his blue down jacket and knit cap, rosy-cheeked, squinting in the winter sun. He held his beleaguered Bubba lion-cub, tight in one fist and smiled up at me. "Where we go-wing?"

"To the mailbox, my love." I tugged his hat down over his ears, kissed the top of his head, and we were off. Trees naked in the sun, shadow branches crisscrossing the sidewalk as we traversed the few blocks from our house to the post box on the corner at 42nd Avenue.

I made our cards every year, but this year they were different. Gone, the happy foursome, Molly and Finn and Charlie and me. Nope, no family photo this year, just a shot of our house. Plain and simple. Our front door hung with the wreath I'd bought at the school fundraiser. And this year, instead of the usual greeting, *Merry Christmas, Happy New Year*, I had folded copies of Rumi's poem, "The Guest House," into every card.

Standing in front of the mailbox, Finn looking up at me, I opened the chute and dumped all those handmade cards in with a shuffle. I listened as my cards landed with a muffled thud on top of the all the others—Christmas cards I imagined filled with holiday epistles telling of family successes, scholastic honors, and athletic achievements. And there on top of that heap were mine, all containing my personal proclamation, Rumi's poem, and my secret pledge: I would embrace this horrible heartbreak and welcome all it had to teach me. And I would never again ignore my intuition. Ever.

"There. We did it. It's done."

Finn lifted Bubba in a victory dance. "Yay! Mommy, we did it!"

―――――

The Guest House

This being human is a guest house.
Every morning a new arrival.
A joy, a depression, a meanness,
some momentary awareness comes
as an unexpected visitor.

Welcome and entertain them all!
Even if they're a crowd of sorrows,
who violently sweep your house
empty of its furniture,
still, treat each guest honorably.
He may be clearing you out
for some new delight.

The dark thought, the shame, the malice,
meet them at the door laughing,
and invite them in.

Be grateful for whoever comes,
because each has been sent as a guide from beyond.
—Rumi

―――――

37

THE WAKE-UP CALL

The breeze at dawn has secrets to tell you.
Don't go back to sleep.
—Rumi

I'd been lying awake for hours, waiting for the dawn to break through the gray, waterlogged blanket that had settled over Portland in November. It was January now, and I was listening to the rain hit the roof and the windows at either end of our cavernous bedroom like an unrelenting hail of bullets.

4:44 am. Again. My nightly attempt to sleep, to tamp my anxiety over life, as I now knew it, impossible. I'd given up on forgiving Charlie. Trust? No way. The task at hand: to forgive myself. I struggled with my exit plan. I was determined to stay in the house with the kids. He would not leave, said he still loved me, begged for forgiveness, and promised to be true. So, there I was in this bed, his lies in my head, a knotted refrain that played through my brain. I prayed my one-word mantra to Mary. My anxious feet twisting the sheets while he slept.

"Kathy! Pick up the phone! Kath, please! Pick up!" I heard my mother call my childhood name through our bedroom. Her voice ricocheted from the answering machine where it sat on a little side table next to the loveseat. That table sagged under a stack of books; their titles charting my way through the last few months. *After the Affair*, and *How to Survive Adultery*, were sandwiched between volumes of Rumi and Hafiz, my true guides.

"Honey! Please!" I pulled myself from the bed, stumbled across the room and lifted the receiver.

"Mom! Geez, it's 5am!" I imagined my mother, a petite English teacher, more grammatical dictator, one thousand miles to the south, sitting at her dining room table surrounded on three sides by bookshelves. Hundreds of books piled three-deep, precariously perched, and threatening to kill her in the next big quake.

"I waited a whole hour! Oh honey. There's a story on the front page of the LA Times this morning. Oh-Dear-God-Kath."

"Mom, what is it?"

"The article claims the President is having an affair with a White House intern."

"Yeah? So?"

"Honey, the intern, it's Mallory."

I dropped the phone and grabbed *Surviving Adultery*, from that teetering stack of books, and sent it flying at the slumbering cheat, hitting him squarely in the head.

"What the fuck!" Charlie shouted.

"Mallory's having an affair with the president!"

"So?"

"Do you have any idea what's going to happen to us now?"

"She's slept with lots of married men. What would they want with us?"

"This is the President of the United States, Charlie."

Somehow, in that moment, I knew they'd come for us.

By the end of that day our answering machine, which usually recorded carpool questions and potluck plans, was clogged to capacity.

"This is Jack Jones from *Extra*." BEEP!

"Hello this is Larry Flint, I'm willing to pay for any information you have." BEEP!

"Malcolm Boyd, *Hard Copy*." BEEP!

"Amy Goldstein with *The Washington Post*...Todd Murphy, *The NY Times*" BEEP! BEEP! BEEP! BEEEEEEEEP!

It all happened so fast, like a tornado with no warning, no time to wonder how they'd found us.

———

The crowds were growing on Knott Street. A slow, steady prowl of cars and vans passed by our house. The phone rang relentlessly. "We know you're in there!" Hard Copy Guy yelled, hung up, and called again, repeatedly. His voice was joined by a chorus of others, broadcast continuously from the answering machine. All begging for sound bites regarding my husband's affair with the president's mistress.

I packed our bags. I paced the floors, Mary-Mary-Mary-Mary. Short of breath, I watched from behind the drapes now drawn tight over the windows that faced out on Knott Street. A handful of cars had spent the day camped out across the road. Sooner or later, they'd have to take a break, I reasoned. Molly knew something was up. I'd put her in charge of Finn; she fed one video after another into the VCR, a steady diet of Disney distraction. Finally, at five pm the last suspicious vehicle slunk away from the curb.

"Come on, kids! Let's go!" Just then the back door opened, and Charlie slid in. *Damn.* I'd hoped to be gone before he got home.

"Man! It's crazy out there, I had to scale the back fence." His eyes landed on the suitcases stacked by the door. "Where are you going?"

Ignoring him, I gathered the bags, the kids, the stroller, my purse, and rushed us out the door across the front porch into the rain.

Out in the driveway, I ducked Finn into his car seat. "Charlie, if there are things you haven't told me, you better come clean now!"

"Momma, where's Bubba?" I pulled Bubba from my big shoulder bag and tucked it into his lap, kissed Finn's head and strapped him in.

"Molly, climb in! Buckle up!"

"Mom, where are we going?" Molly climbed into the back seat next to Finn.

I stormed past Charlie, now standing next to the car watching as I loaded our suitcases into the trunk and slammed it shut.

"I swear, Charlie, if I read anything in the papers you haven't already admitted."

"I've told you everything! Please don't leave!"

I jumped into the driver's seat, slammed the door, and peeled out of the driveway with a screech. Heart drumming my chest, I sped off down Knott Street steadying myself, hands tight on the wheel, checking the rearview for traces of a tail. My antique rosary swinging from its loop around that mirror—a mother-of-pearl metronome. *Mary, please help.* We hurtled past the mailbox where just one month before, Finn and I made our triumphant deposit. "Welcome and entertain them all! Even if they are a crowd of sorrows..." *Oh, Rumi,* I mumbled, *I thought you meant his other women.*

"Mom, where are we going?" Molly called from the back seat.

"LA, honey. We'll see Marina, and you'll see your dad."

Like refugees. We fled.

We were four hours early for our flight, no matter, waiting at the airport felt safer than home. "Molly, honey, I need you to push Finn." I touched her cheek and kissed her head. *Breathe,* I told myself, *breathe.* I plopped Finn's padded rear into the stroller. He held Bubba tight. Molly belted him in. I heaved the bags up and out of the trunk. We trekked to the terminal. I bought our tickets, maxing out the credit card. I checked us in and then corralled the kids to the food court. It was deserted. Thank God. I chose a table that was tucked out of sight and fed the kids a hasty supper of lousy airport food, a greasy mix of chicken strips and tater tots. A treat for them. A transgression for me.

"Airpane! Momma! Airpane!" Finn pointed out the windows that lined the wall, to the huge jets taxiing on the runway. Just then, the setting sun broke through a dark bank of clouds and bright beams shimmered the wet-black tarmac golden. Mary-Mary-Mary. I tried see the promise in those sunbeams, but that blinding yellow made me squint as it spilled across the food court floor and mixed with the eerie glow of enormous TV screens. They were everywhere. All broadcasted Mallory's exploits with the President and the Portland connection to the story. My husband. Their father. I did my best to distract the kids.

"Look! Mommy! It's Mallory." Molly's eyes flashed surprise

as she pointed to the giant screen closest to our table in the food court. My gut roiled. There she was, Mallory, in her blue beret, standing in that blasted receiving line, smiling up at the President—the same footage screening over and over in one continuous loop. "Mommy, why?"

"I'll tell you later, Molly. Let's go to Powell's!" I bussed our table, and we crossed the concourse, a huddled cluster. Molly kept her hand tight to one side of Finn's stroller. Finn kept his hand tight on Bubba, and I piloted all three of us into the airport Powell's Books, a TV-free oasis filled with books and games and puzzles. I unleashed the kids. "Pick three things each!"

"Yay!" they chorused. While they collected their goodies, I collected mine. I gathered every newspaper I could get my hands on. *NY Times, Washington Post, LA Times,* even *The Oregonian.* I paid the clerk and stuffed them all in my carry on. And off we trailed in the direction of our gate.

"Airpane! Momma! Airpane!" Finn pointed wildly in the direction of the giant faux fuselage in the children's play area. I glanced at my watch.

"Okay," I said. "Molly, you watch Finn. I need to make a call." I ducked into a nearby phone booth, keeping them in my sightline, and lifted the receiver to make the call I'd been dreading. Over the last several months, while I'd shared the mess of my marriage with my mother, I'd kept it from my father. But I did not want him to read it in the paper or see it on TV. It was time.

"Hi, Dad, it's Kath."

"Hi, Honey, how are ya?"

"Dad, I don't know if you've been watching the news. Have you heard about the president's affair with a white house intern?"

"Yeah, what a mess that is!"

"Well, have you heard anything about a connection to Port-land? A teacher?"

"Oh yeah, I think I heard something about that."

"Dad, that teacher? It's Charlie."

"What? *Your* Charlie? Oh, sweetheart. Oh, Kath, God, I'm so sorry. Listen, sit tight. I'll call you right back, I'm going to call my brother." My dad's little brother, my favorite uncle, Mitch, was a press crisis manager, a fixer who spent his time getting politicians and assorted celebrities out of hot water.

"Dad?" The dial tone sounded in my ear.

I glanced at my watch. "Molly, Finn, its time! Let's go!"

At long last, we tucked into our seats on the last flight that night out of Portland to LAX. Safely sealed in that plane, I massaged the knot in my shoulders, buckled us in, and rifled through my carry-on to dig out our distractions. As soon as Molly and Finn were occupied with their new treasures, I settled in for a good long read. The two and a half hours to LAX was plenty of time to get caught up, to fill in the blanks.

38

NIGHT FLIGHT

The plane banked and tipped a wave through my gut. Adrenalin surged my nerves. My heart beat its broken rhythm. Mary-Mary-Mary. My fingers were blackened with newsprint—proof of my husband's lies, interviews with his former Beverly Hills High School students, and co-workers all telling more than he'd told. Seems everyone knew what he'd been up to. Except me.

There is nothing quite like public shame. You know the dream; you've shown up naked at school, people point and laugh. Or you're wide awake, attending an event and discover later your fly is wide open. Or worse, you exit a public restroom, and the hem of your dress is caught in the waistband of your pantyhose and you cross the room with your rear-end on display in a nylon sausage casing.

But this? I would keep my pledge to listen, to learn, and to trust my gut. But now my private heartbreak would be a public hell. My shame and humiliation on view for all to see, amidst a growing cast of characters. Not just my husband and his other women, but the president and his—the one they shared.

I watched out the window, and there she was, my birthplace. That city of the angels. So hell-bent I was on leaving her, and so sorry now.

It's best to arrive in LA by night. In the light of day, her smoggy sprawl, a crosshatched tattoo of asphalt and concrete, can overwhelm and depress. But by night, she is a magic fairy kingdom decked out in her finery. Lights float out for miles like earthbound stars. Even the crisscross of freeways: by day, clogged ailing arteries; but in the darkness, those taillights unfurl like glowing party streamers to welcome me home.

The landing gear cranked into position and sent a jolt through my heart. We made our slow descent. Molly and Finn were asleep in their seats, two tousled heads bookending my shoulders. I nudged them and they stirred, yet clung to sleep. "We're here." I whispered as I stuffed my rumpled newspapers into my carry-on.

Mary-Mary-Mary. Please send angels.

That night my angel was Marina. She waited at the gate as we deplaned. We were a clump of ruffled refugees. Two sleepy-heads and mine, buzzing with fear. Timmy, up long past his bedtime, jumped up and down and grabbed Finn around the neck in a sweet, rambunctious four-year-old reunion. Marina held me. I hugged her tight. Her dark, wild, wavy tresses tickled my nose. I breathed the fragrance of her. A wild rose this one, mixed with some unnamable spicy scent that clung to her hair, a remnant of what she'd cooked for dinner. A sob threatened to escape my lungs. "Oh girl," she whispered in my ear as she rubbed my back. I wanted to collapse into her, but held myself steady. Molly's arms encircled Marina's waist. "Hey Molly!" Marina laughed her sandpapered laugh.

"Thanks, Marina. Hope Nick doesn't mind."

"Nope. He left on business this morning, perfect timing."

Marina piloted her big black SUV up the wind of canyon road that climbed the hills to her house. Her hidden hacienda sat high above Brentwood and Pacific Palisades. Nestled in sage-covered slopes, her home was cradled in a lush landscape that she had filled with a wild cascade of roses—all white. This place would be my safe house, a walled fortress where I could hide and think and breathe.

We pulled into the drive. I wrestled our bags from the hatch while Marina unlocked the carved wooden doors, nine feet tall, which opened into her secret garden. We stepped inside, and those doors slammed shut behind us. Locked tight. Safe. The courtyard was paved with terracotta tiles, that framed the lap pool. It glowed silver in the moonlight. A filigree of white roses entwined with magenta bougainvillea and ivy, climbed the walls.

We dragged the bags to the guest room, situated in the wing opposite the main house on the other side of the pool. A hidden haven for three weary travelers. Marina had prepared the room; white roses toppled the rim of a cobalt blue vase she'd placed on the bedside table. The bed, king-sized, was layered in white down comforters and pillows. "Thank you, Marina." A tear slipped down my cheek; she caught it with the tip of her slender finger and nodded with a knowing smile.

"Time for bed," Marina called to Timmy, "you'll play in the morning." She hiked her sleepy boy to her hip and headed out the French doors that faced the pool and nodded to me as she carted Timmy out the door, "I'll meet you in the house."

I tucked Molly and Finn into bed. They sank into that downy nest; I kissed their foreheads and threaded my fingers through their hair. "Sleep, my loveys," I whispered, and they tumbled into deep sleep.

Newsprint evidence in hand, I skirted the edges of the pool

towards the main house. I breathed the air, and there it was, that scent I'd longed for. Night blooming jasmine perfumed the January dark.

Marina's home was an old friend. The entire first floor was open, living room, dining room, and kitchen. Ten sets of French doors lined the room on every side. Now it was black with night, but by day, those windowed doors brought the outside in. This house *was* Marina: a riot of color, a treasure chest of antiques, hand-blown glass, and soft light that glowed from lamps and silken lampshades. Every surface was wrapped in ethnic textiles: Guatemala, India, and Tibet. Turkish rugs floated on the terracotta floors.

I tossed the newspapers on the coffee table in front of the fire. Flames crackled and glowed warmth from the hearth. I grabbed the fuzzy purple throw off the back of the sofa and wrapped myself in it. I tried to sit but couldn't. I paced the room, dragging the afghan behind me. My footsteps tracing the edges of the room.

I walked my Mary meditation. Mary-Mary-Mary-Mary.

Marina's voice, deep and throaty, drifted a tune down the stairs from Timmy's room, "Moon River," his favorite lullaby. "We're after the same rainbow's end, my huckleberry friend..." Marina, still singing, padded down the stairs at the far end of the room. She wore silk pajamas in a wild floral print. Her hair, caught in a thick frizzy knot on top of her head. I loved this woman.

Marina hummed her way to the kitchen, grabbed two goblets from the cupboard and pulled a pitcher out of the fridge. Ice clinked the glasses. "I made your sangria!" She poured a healthy dose into each glass, headed to the couch, and set them down next to the newspapers on the coffee table. "Come. Sit," she called as I paced the room. She patted my spot on the sofa with the palm of her hand.

I wandered over and flopped beside her. A sob escaped my lungs. Marina handed me a box of tissues with one hand and a glass of sangria with the other. "Drink," she said. I took a swig and felt the cool slide down my throat: tart, sweet, and potent.

I pointed to the stack of newspapers. "Extra! Extra! Read all about it!" I choked a laugh through my tears.

"Ooooh, Girl! You just be having yourself a big ol' life!" We laughed—hers throaty, mine wet. "Yep. You just be havin' a big ol' life."

39

NO COMMENT

By the time I wrestled myself from sleep the next morning, the kids had left the bed. I could hear their happy voices outside in the sun. Marina had squeezed fresh O.J. and made pancakes for the kids. They ate their breakfast poolside. Finn and Timmy retreated to the wooden fort in the back corner of the yard. Molly and Marina sat at the patio table and painted each other's fingernails. Every nail a different color—tiny jewels capping twenty fingers. They giggled and chattered. Marina was Molly's fairy godmother.

"Morning," I said, the sun squinting my eyes as I shuffled into the kitchen. The big sliding window above the kitchen sink was wide open to the sun, and the counter beneath it held a buffet of fresh fruit, yogurt, and buttery croissants.

"Eat." Marina pointed.

"Can't," I replied. I chose a mug from the cupboard and filled it with hot coffee, added cream, and headed back out into the courtyard. The morning was chilly in the shade but warm in the sun. I dragged a chair to a sunny spot and lifted my face to greet that stranger. How I'd missed this winter warmth. Sun flooded my face like a ravished kiss from a long-lost lover. The air was full of roses and sage. Bright sunlight skittered a searchlight across the pool to find me. I could almost imagine the sun had missed me too.

Marina pulled a chair up next to mine. "Ya sleep?"

"I did." Miraculous. I'd missed my four am wake up call, that built-in buzzer fueled by anxiety. But now awake, it settled in, I could not wall it out, even here, in this place I loved.

"Whatcha gonna do?"

"Don't know," I said. "Everything hurts like a bad flu. I need to think and make a plan." The phone rang. Anxiety grabbed me by the neck. Marina headed to answer.

"It's Charlie," she mouthed her hand over the receiver. I shook my head. NO.

"She's in the shower," I heard her say.

Back in the kitchen I refilled my cup and stopped to look at the pictures Marina had pinned to the corkboard. Amidst the photos of friends and family, was the Rumi poem I'd folded into my Christmas card just last month.

"Welcome and entertain them all! Even if they are a crowd of sorrows, who violently sweep your house empty of its furniture..."

This time a buzzer cracked the fragile calm. Marina headed to the intercom.

"It's Hank," she buzzed him in.

"Molly, your dad's here, let's get your stuff."

"Ohhhh noooooo, too soon!" she waved her fingernails through the air. "They're not even dry yet!"

There he was—my first mistake. I braced myself for his contempt and criticism, always at the helm. "Kate, what the hell? I had reporters at my door this morning. They peppered me with questions about you, about Charlie."

"*Your* door? What did you say?"

"The only thing to say: No comment. Look, I'll keep Molly with me till this blows over; we'll stay in a hotel. But sooner or later you'll have to make a statement. Till then, two words: No comment." Hank's eyes held no harm but instead an unexpected kindness. And just like that, my first husband climbed a little rung somewhere in my heart, a tiny promotion. And he knew it, I saw it in his eyes, a flicker that read, "See? I'm not so bad. At least I didn't cheat on you."

No comment. Two handy, helpful words that I would repeat countless times over the next two years.

———

Hank and Molly trailed out the door and, right on cue, that damn phone rang. I bristled with anxiety and looked to Marina, her hand over the receiver. "Charlie," she mouthed with a hike of her brow. I winced and then shrugged. I took the cordless phone from her hand and trudged a diagonal path from the kitchen across her sun-splashed floors to the back corner of the great room, headed for the privacy of the powder room. Concerned someone might need it, I made a quick U-turn and ducked into a closet, stepped inside, and pulled the door shut. A pitch-black soundproof booth for my fury.

"You liar, you asshole!" I shouted into that darkness. "You swore you'd told me everything. The entire student body of Beverly Hills High School knew what you were up to!"

"Kate. I'm so sorry. Please come home. I need you. We'll face this together. I'll be a better man, I promise."

40

THE CLOSET

Despite the January sun that streamed across Marina's terracotta floors, I set up camp in the closet. There were no clothes in this closet. No coats, no hats, no boots, or umbrellas. Just music. This closet, a large walk-in, was home to Nick and Marina's extensive music library. Hundreds of CDs, housed in jewel cases, sat silently on custom-built shelves, ready to spin songs. Songs of love and devotion and heartbreak.

Music. The irony not lost on me, I sat on the floor, and I faced it.

Soundproof, the perfect container for my grief. Total darkness, save for a seam of light where the door met the floor. A switch in the jam extinguished the fixture overhead when the door was pulled shut. Knowing this, Marina shuttled supplies. A small antique lamp with a stained-glass shade threw rainbows on the walls. A stack of Turkish cushions softened my spot on the floor. A thick pad of paper and pens—all colors—to list pros and cons.

I've never been good at pros and cons. Creating such a list always induced a mild panic in me. What if I made the wrong choice despite those columns? What about weighted entries? What if the pros were really cons? Just like my husband.

Laying pros and cons aside, I started by outlining my situation thus far.

1. Face it. Your marriage is a sham. Your beloved has cheated on you with not just one, but with two "other women," and possibly—probably—more, for the entire length of your marriage.

2. Your friend, Mallory, is not a friend at all. This "friend" you confided in during all those dark months of doubt and suspicion, was all the while sleeping with your husband, milking you for details, reporting all back to him. A spy, in babysitter's clothing.

And now...

3. A bizarre coincidence? You admit you're prone to look for meaning in coincidences. But this? Your husband's mistress has taken up with another married man, the leader of the free world. What is the meaning of this?

4. Consequences. You've been forced from your home. The home you have longed for all your life, is now surrounded by a media sorrow circus, hungry mobs all dying for a morsel to add to this sordid stew.

5. The Vow. You made a vow of "for better or for worse." Is this the "worse" they warn of? Can it get worse than this? Do you keep the promise you made to yourself? To stick this marriage out no matter what? Two marriages okay, two divorces —no way.

———

Exhausted, I laid my notepad aside, grabbed the phone from the floor and checked my home answering machine for messages. Voicemail full, and there, amidst the throngs of reporters, I heard my father's voice. "Honey, where are you? Call me." I picked up the phone and dialed.

"Dad, it's Kath."

"Honey, where are you?"

"LA."

"LA? Your uncle Mitch is in Portland. He flew up there to help you." My father's call for help had caught my uncle on the freeway. He'd just landed at LAX and was headed south on the 405, home to Laguna. When my dad told him what was happening, he took the next exit, headed north, and hopped the next flight out of LAX bound for Portland.

"Write down this number, he's waiting for your call."

I dialed my uncle. "Where are you?" he asked.

"Hiding," I said, "in LA."

"Okay, that's funny, I'm in Portland. Tell me what's happening."

I told my uncle everything I knew.

"I can help, but you'll have to come home. I know the press, and they won't go away until you give them something. Come home, and I'll see you through this."

———

For the next two days, I prayed and wept in the closet. My eyes burned, swollen with grief. If I'd known how to gnash my teeth, I'd have done it.

In that moment, my ability to see Mallory as a victim was hampered by my fury at her betrayal. All these years later, I see things differently.

Thing is, I'd been in Mallory's spot years ago. At the age of sixteen I had a fling with a high school teacher. He was unmarried and twice my age. A handsome bachelor, he was also an elder in my church and my youth group leader. After I'd completed his class as a sophomore, he asked if I'd be his TA during my junior year.

I can still recall the day I first reported for duty. The cold fluorescent light in his windowless box of an office, the heat flushing my face as his eyes traveled a vertical path from my platform sandals, up the length of my 70s bell bottoms to the shirt I'd worn that day, patterned with cherries—red buttons straining across my burgeoning chest. And then his smile—a rakish grin—and the heat in my cheeks when our eyes finally met.

Before long he was offering to drive me home in the evenings after our youth group meetings. Sitting in his car in the dark at the bottom of my long driveway, he'd ask how things were going at home. His sincere attention and concern were flattering, and I gladly confided my struggles at home.

It was during one of these driveway moments, when he first leaned in for a kiss. He apologized, but that kiss led to another. Those kisses lit a fire—a fire that soon had me sneaking to his apartment after school and lying to my parents about my whereabouts. He employed all the standard tricks, declaring his desire, his need for me. He swore me to a secrecy that served to separate me from my friends—an isolation that fostered depression.

Our encounter was over in a matter of months. When I heard the rumors that he had a pattern of preying on high school girls, I understood I was not the only one. I realized my school-girl fantasies of being the one he'd finally marry were just that—fantasies. He was getting what he wanted. I would not. So, despite his pleading, I broke things off. In the end, when the story came out, I was faulted for being an oversexed teenager—a 16-year-old seductress. He went scot-free. As women, we know this story well.

I understand the challenges of my childhood had created a

fierce need for attention and touch. As a teenager, attention from boys filled a void. The attention of an older man was intoxicating. That a "man" would risk his career, his standing in the community and his church, to be with me, was powerful medicine for a young girl who longed for approval and acceptance. It would be many years before I saw myself as a victim. At the age of sixteen, I felt as teenagers often do, all powerful. I did not have the capacity to see an older man's desire for me in terms of right or wrong. I only felt flattered and wanted.

All these years later, I can imagine what my teacher saw in me that was so easily exploited, was much the same thing Charlie saw in Mallory. A young woman, hungry for approval and vulnerable to the attentions of older men.

I sat on the floor in the closet. The only way out was through. My mind was a battlefield, my heart, a shattered platter. Mary, Mary, Mary. Charlie's women were one thing. But why had I landed in the middle of this national scandal? What was I meant to learn?

I have always searched for meaning in things. Have done so since I was a child. Remember those grasses that bent in the breeze? I'd wrongly believed their example would serve me, that I would survive this life if only I followed the whim of the winds. The result? I had no will of my own. It was clear this belief no longer served me. Perhaps the beliefs we adopt in childhood serve us in childhood; but as adults, those adaptations no longer benefit. Agency—the ability to stand on my own, make my own choices, and to trust myself, my gut, these were the skills I needed to hone.

And what of these men I had chosen? The men I'd hoped would love and protect me had deserted and betrayed me instead. Had it been my childhood that taught me I did not deserve better? If I *were* here to learn, I would learn this: Self-deception is the first betrayal. I had betrayed myself by ignoring that whispered hint of intuition, by marrying a man I'd suspected I could not trust.

I had committed other self-betrayals, had dismissed my intuition before. Back while living with Hank, pregnant with Molly, I had not felt safe in our Venice Beach apartment. Despite my repeated pleas to Hank that we needed to move, I let his constant argument that my premonitions were silly, win. I had disregarded the persistent feeling I was not safe and I stayed. And then a rapist climbed through my window.

I survived the rape—that brute force did not break me. I searched for meaning there too. One week before I gave birth, my babe heavy in the cradle of my hips, I attended my attacker's arraignment. I sat in the witness stand with the evidence of his brutality still visible in a jagged ring of bruises around my neck and made my statement to the judge. "I begged this man—please I can't breathe—if I can't breathe, my baby can't breathe—she will die—if she dies, I want to die." I said this all while my rapist sat shackled, just a few feet away, leering at me.

My need to write my ending to that horror drove me to that witness stand. My desire to see that man jailed overrode my fear of facing him. Months later, I would go to the sentencing too. This time, all the young mothers from my baby group would sit in that courtroom as I made my statement. Despite my panic attack that morning, I would beg the judge for the harshest sentence possible. I stood up to my rapist, confronted him and the trauma of the rape again.

In the end, I would face this assault too.

I grabbed my tattered copy of "The Essential Rumi" from the closet floor and flipped it open to read this:

"Unfold your own myth...start walking. Your legs will get heavy

and tired. Then comes a moment of feeling the wings you've grown, lifting."

For better or worse, I decided to return home. I would stand up in this moment. I would face this thing. I would not run. I would not desert myself. I would not repeat my self-betrayal. I would squeeze every drop of meaning from this crazy place I'd landed in, and I would forge my way through it with hopes of growing those wings.

But before I emerged from the closet, I cut a deal with Rumi. I would confront this thing, I would welcome it all, but I would hold him to the promise of his poem. If this crowd of sorrows were indeed a gift, then I would expect him to deliver on his promise of a "new delight."

Rumi said, "Unfold your own myth."

Challenge accepted—I would do it.

41

UNCLE MITCH TO THE RESCUE

"Apologies folks, it's gonna be a bumpy ride. Please remain seated with your seatbelts fastened for the remainder of the flight." My neck was in knots, knuckles white long before the pilot's announcement.

The plane pitched and dropped. My stomach rolled. I snugged Finn's seatbelt around his middle. He held his Bubba in one hand and clenched mine with the other.

"We're gonna be fine." I smiled into his saucer-wide eyes.

Fine. I repeated to myself. *Just fine.* In truth, I was terrified.

Charlie waited for us at the gate. Bile backed up my throat at the sight of him. He leaned in for a hug, I stiffened. He shrugged and lifted Finn to his hip, snuggled into him.

"I'm so glad you're home," he said. "I can't believe this is happening."

I could. The moment of my mother's call, I knew they'd come for us. But this magnitude? This craziness? I could not have imagined this.

Charlie drove the long way around, avoiding our neighborhood altogether. We headed to our hideout in silence. I explained to Finn that we weren't going home; we were spending the night at Penny and Josh's house.

"A sleepover party," I enthused but fell short. I longed to go home, to sleep in my own bed, to tuck Finn into his. But our home was in occupied territory, so we went to our "safe house" instead.

Uncle Mitch was waiting for us there when we arrived. He gathered me into his arms as I came through the door. I fell into him with a muffled cry.

"You'll get through this," he whispered, rubbing my back. "I'm here." It had been a few years since I'd seen him last. His thick brown hair, now threaded gray at his temples, looked good on him. The salt and pepper set off his vibrant blue eyes, eyes that always had a rakish twinkle. "Quite a mess you're in," he chuckled, giving me another squeeze.

Coats off, Finn settled, we sat in a ring round the cozy living room. Our catastrophe had converted Penny and Josh's house into command central. Our mess now infected their home. Corey and Richard were there too, for added support.

Uncle Mitch sat forward in this chair, "I surveilled the house before coming here. Satellite trucks, news vans, the entire block is jammed. Side streets too. I don't know who sicced the press on you, but they've set up camp, and in my experience, they will not go away till you make a statement. Charlie, tell me what you know."

Charlie started with his affair. "I tried to break things off with her, but she would always threaten to tell Kate if I did." *Yeah right,* I thought, *but maybe so.*

What we knew of Mallory in Washington, D.C., all came courtesy of Mallory herself. She had told one lover, my husband, all the gory details about her sexual adventures with another, detailing her White House escapades, stories of sexual encounters with a "high ranking" White House official. "She never named him," Charlie said, leaning forward in his chair, hands gripping his knees. "She called him the Creep. She told me the Creep did her with a cigar."

"She told you what?" I held my arms tight around my middle. What a fool I'd been. Charlie had explained those long, hushed kitchen conversations as Mallory's need for his advice regarding a frustrating relationship with a new boyfriend in DC. All those nights, while I haplessly bathed our kids and read bedtime stories, Charlie was perched on the step stool in the kitchen listening as Mallory plied her lover—my husband— with her own bedtime stories.

I watched as Charlie recounted these stories to my uncle, he was oddly energized, excited even. Why? *To be in the know?*

Mitch turned to me.

I nervously recounted her daily calls from the White House, which I now understood were a ruse to gauge my mounting suspicions about Charlie's infidelity and report all back to him.

She had told me more than once how handsome the president was, how charismatic, how sexy. One day she'd called from the White House. "Quick, turn on CNN," she said. "The president is wearing my tie!" She told me she'd given the president a necktie as a gift and expressed her annoyance that he hadn't thanked her yet. The fact that he wore it to sign a piece of legislation, was, she explained, a signal and the thank you she'd been waiting for.

I listed all the stuff she'd sent us, signed photos of the president inscribed to Molly and Finn, to Charlie and to me. All arrived in periodic care packages. She'd sent White House M&M's and White House matches, the president's favorite recipe on a recipe card engraved with the presidential seal. Chicken enchiladas.

"It's clear that Mallory has told you things that put you in a compromised position. It's also clear she has a pattern of sleeping with married men and the two of you have information to prove it," Mitch counseled. "If you want your life to get back to anything near normal, you will have to make a statement. The press will not go away until you do. I suggest we schedule a press conference and soon." Charlie nodded his head in agreement, then turned to our friends and to me, all of us stunned by the enormity of our situation.

"Can I take some time to think about it?" I asked my uncle.

"Yes, but don't take too long. You want to do this on your terms."

"I'll call you in the morning," I said. "Mitch, thank you."

"Try to get some sleep." He stood, gave me another long hug, and headed out the door.

———

Later that night, all of us sat huddled in front of Penny and Josh's television. We waited for the president to speak. This presidential press conference promised to address our leader's affair with his White House intern. It was, in fact, an oracle that would determine my course of action. I hoped to forgo my uncle's suggestion, to avoid going public.

I sat in the armchair across the room, as far from Charlie as possible. He sat, sandwiched between Penny and Josh, on the couch. Corey perched on the arm of my chair and rubbed my back.

Arms wrapped tight around my middle, I was sick with shock and worry. I tried to breathe and waited for the president to own up and tell America the truth about Mallory; to rescue us from the media circus that surrounded our home.

When, at last, our president flooded the small screen in the corner of the living room and pointed just one of his guilty fingers at all of America and spoke those now infamous words, "I did not have sexual relations with that woman," I knew life would be hell. His truth had the power to save us from this public shame, from the hounds that surrounded our home. His lie would chart the course for his impeachment and set the stage for our long-term humiliation. Yes, the press would have still wanted the details of my husband's affair with the president's intern, but soon, they would have moved on.

"Well, that's it." I glared at the other liar in the room. "We're toast."

———

Sleep was impossible. Thoughts rolled over me in the guest bed in Penny and Josh's dark basement. The only light, the bedside clock, blinked 3:33 am.

We had to come forward—for all kinds of reasons. I thought I knew something important. I knew Mallory to be someone who had no qualms about carrying on an affair with a married man. Who knew what Charlie's motivation was; I can't know all these years later. He had promised to be better man, and perhaps, in some way, he thought he *was* better because he would stand in front of America and admit his adultery while our leader, the other married man, would not.

I desperately wanted life to get back to normal, whatever normal would be going forward. I wanted Molly to come home. I wanted my kids to sleep in their beds, with their books on their nightstands beside them. I wanted to go home.

———

The next morning, exhausted from another sleepless night, Finn on my hip, I stepped out onto Penny and Josh's front porch to get some air. A camera flashed and a man rushed towards me from across the street, microphone in one hand, business card in the other.

"Ma'am, I'm from 60 Minutes. We'd like to do a respectful interview with you and your husband."

"No comment," I practiced.

"Please consider it." I took his card and turned to go back inside. "Hey," he called out, "we've been feeding your cats." *Our poor cats.*

"Thanks for that," I ducked back through the door.

"They're feeding our cats."

"What?" Charlie was busy shoveling Cheerios into his mouth.

"They've found us." I handed him the business card. "I'm calling Uncle Mitch. I want to go home."

42

FACE THE NATION

I t was January-dark, and of course, there was rain. Always the rain.

The short drive from our "safe house" to the house on Knott Street was untenably long. Mary-Mary-Mary. I prayed my mantra in the back seat where I perched next to Finn, hoping to protect him. Bright camera lights flashed upon our return. I raised my open palm to Finn's eyes, an attempt to shield him, but I couldn't shield my four-year-old from what was happening. His father's ability to lie and cheat had brought us to this.

Our narrow, tree-lined street was clogged with vehicles. Aliens had overtaken the neighborhood; satellite dishes swiveled and whirled above our picturesque block. The road vibrated with the rumbled hum of generators spewing diesel fumes into the air.

Charlie swung the car into our driveway. We waited, as instructed, with the car doors locked tight. Reporters surged and surrounded our car. My uncle pulled in behind us, jumped out of his vehicle and addressed the crowd.

"Stand back!" he commanded. "Let them pass." He motioned for us to step from the car, but as we unlocked the doors, they charged us again. The whole stormy sea of them, a tidal wave rushing in to swallow us whole. "Stand back!" my uncle repeated. "Please give my clients an opportunity to get their child into the house," his arms outstretched, a human stanchion. "Okay, let's go!" he yelled, directing us to exit the car.

Charlie, oddly calm, stepped into the driveway. He lifted Finn from his car seat and handed him to me. We rushed to the door, lights strobing at our backs. Mitch in a wide stance, necktie blowing in the wind and rain, held the mob at bay while Charlie fumbled with the keys and at last unlocked the front door.

My heart galloped in my chest, I was all nerves and ragged breathing, a fear-based clanging in my skull. To see my home surrounded like a crime scene, the lights and sounds of this night conjured police cruisers and ambulance rides, this siege reactivating my PTSD. Long ago, I was forced from my home by a rapist and never returned. Despite my fear, I was determined, I would not lose this home to these intruders.

Once inside, I handed Finn back to his father and ran from room to room. I pulled the draperies tight over all the windows, grabbed a stack of tablecloths from the linen closet and dug thumbtacks out of the kitchen junk drawer. I raced to cover the windowed top half of our front door. Panic surged as I dragged a stool to reach the window over the kitchen sink to cover it. Someone in the driveway snapped a photo, blinding me. I stumbled to the French doors in the nook, someone had scaled the back fence, lights flashed from the yard as I tacked a tablecloth over them as well. I rushed to close the blinds in the kid's rooms that faced the backyard. Penny and Josh arrived to lend support and care for Finn, while we prepared to make our statement.

My uncle had spent the day notifying the press that we

would make a statement that evening. The press conference was set for six pm. My uncle's associate, a high-profile lawyer, had flown in from Los Angeles to advise us. For better or worse, he would be our spokesman.

We told the lawyer what we'd told Mitch the night before. His thick hair framed a stern face. He outlined what was before us, making notes on a legal pad he'd pulled from his leather briefcase. He reiterated my uncle's view, making it very clear that if we wanted the press to go away, we would have to negotiate this barreling train—this tornado of devastation that my husband, his mistress and her other married man, the American president, had visited on our family, our home.

———

On the night of January 27th, 1998, one night after the president's televised denial, six days after going into hiding, we stepped out onto the front porch of the house on Knott Street into the blinding assault of camera flash, the click-click-click of shutters like pistol fire, to make our statement. I stepped out our front door into that crowd of sorrows, their microphones and video cameras, the brooms they'd use to sweep my home empty of its furniture. My hopes and my heart shredded but still saying YES. Yes, to this mess and to all I was meant to learn.

In photographs from that night, I am seen standing next to my husband, my cheeks flushed red from cold and rage, eyelids swollen from tears and sleeplessness. Still, there I am, forcing a smile. It is a smile I still regret.

Clear across the country in the White House, not my house, but a house just the same, another woman stood next to her husband, and she too was smiling.

Why do we do this? Smile through our pain; endure public humiliation to stand next to these men? My smile masked a deep shame, a harrowing humiliation as I stood next to my husband, an admitted liar and cheat.

Her smile? Only she can speak to that.

Years later, I imagine each of us there for our own reasons. My uncle, out of love for me, coupled with his desire to shepherd his niece through her media nightmare. The lawyer, as a favor to my uncle, though given his follow-up, a weeklong tour of morning talk shows, I imagine he liked the spotlight.

My husband? Though I'd hoped him repentant, looking back at it now, I see this may have been his moment in the spotlight on this twisted world stage. The barely-there smirk on his face in the photos from that night belies a slight bemusement, an expression so familiar to me, a faux innocence in those whitewashed eyes. I read no remorse.

And me? A desire to keep my pledge to myself, coupled with my need to go home, to right this ship, and rebuild my fragile boat.

Unbeknownst to us at the time, CNN had chosen to run our press conference split-screen, opposite the president's 1998 State of the Union Address. Because of this we were accused of grandstanding, accused of attempting to upstage the president for political purposes. Because my uncle was a Republican who'd worked for Nixon before Watergate, we would be accused of being Republicans too, and part of the vast right-wing conspiracy to undermine the presidency.

In fact, I was a devoted Democrat. I had voted for this cheater-in-chief. Twice. Ironic—in casting my vote, I'd voted for another man whose transgressions, along with my husband's, would bring me to this.

Another irony, I will hear years later that the moment we walked out onto our porch was perhaps forced by another conspiracy, not rightwing, but one orchestrated by the president and his first lady, themselves. It has been widely reported that they'd hired a private investigator charged with exposing Mallory as a stalker—not a victim. This brought the press to our door. I wonder if they ever considered that in their effort to protect their house, they'd set mine on fire?

Looking back, I ask myself, would I have repeated things I'd assumed Mallory said to me in jest about the president, had I known my uncle's lawyer would weaponize them and turn them against her? I don't know. I was so blindsided by my husband's affairs and desperate to make sense of her role in my current nightmare, at the time all felt relevant.

I see now, we were part of the ploy, and we played our parts well.

———

"Have you seen the paper?" Uncle Mitch came through the door early the next morning and tossed the latest edition of the Oregonian down in front of me. I sat at my pine table, my eyes swollen with tears, still in my bathrobe, drapes drawn tight.

"You've got a halo, kiddo!" The black and white photo, shot from behind as we stood on the porch the night before, showed scores of reporters like an unruly herd, trampling our flowerbeds and lawn, and there I was standing next to my husband with a mantle of light around my head and shoulders.

"Kinda crooked," I said.

"A halo, just the same." My uncle laughed, placing his hands on my shoulders, and gave me a squeeze.

Charlie came out of Molly's room running his fingers through bed head. Molly still in LA, made separate sleeping quarters a given.

"Just a few stragglers out there this morning," Mitch announced, peeking from behind the drapes to the street. It was mostly quiet out on Knott Street. The satellite trucks and news vans had dispersed, though a few cars sat, staked out across the street.

"Have a seat," Mitch said to Charlie. He pulled a legal pad out of his briefcase and presented us with a long list of names and numbers, all media. He had spent the morning fielding requests for interviews. Most wanted an exclusive with Charlie, though some, Mitch pointed out, were for me. "They want a woman's angle on this." He explained our options, advised us as to which we should consider. I said no to all.

I just wanted them to go away and stay away, but no such luck...

Back in 1994, our first winter in Portland, the lead story for three straight weeks, on the local evening news, was the search for the lost mascot of Timberline Lodge. The Saint Bernard had gone missing on Mt. Hood and search parties slogged through snow and high winds on the mountain desperate to find the beloved pooch. "I hope they find him," I'd said to Charlie, all those years ago. "Gotta love it, though. No murders, no mayhem, just a missing dog."

Now *we* were *that* story. Yes, the press conference had for the most part, cleared the press from our street, but because our front porch had been the local stage in a sideshow to a presidential sex scandal, we would keep the local news organizations busy with the Portland connection for months to come. Every ripple, every rumor, would bring unwelcomed visitors to our door.

For one week solid following the press conference, Charlie was the running gag of late-night monologues. "Have you seen this guy?" Jay Leno asked his audience. "That ponytail? This guy looks like a cross between Michael Bolton and the Hanson Brothers."

43

HELL FOR A SPELL

The bedside-clock that doubled as my digital fortune-teller blinked 4:44 when I rolled to face it that morning. Fourth time this week. I had learned from my study of numerology that the appearance of fours in multiples of three meant there was something to learn. *Ha...I'll say.*

Molly's return to Portland brought Charlie back to our bed. I argued he should sleep on the couch. No luck. I was too exhausted to fight. He maintained a steady snore. How he slept with all that was happening was beyond me. I chalked it up to his continued denial. *Damn him.*

I swiveled my feet to the floor in search of my slippers and grabbed my robe. It hung on me now, wound around my frame twice. In the last few months, twenty-five pounds had fallen off fast. The Stress Diet was what a neighbor had called it when she showed up at my door the day after the press conference to apologize for being among the throngs of reporters and neighbors who had trampled our front lawn. I'd seen her there on the edge of the mayhem, her mouth hanging open with shock as Charlie confessed his sins.

I cinched my robe and headed toward the stairs. Out the second story window, the morning was still dark. Dawn—a tiny streak of pinkish light—struggled to crack the gray horizon line. Down the stairs, the house was cold and silent. I lit the chandelier low, turned the furnace high. I longed for my secret sanctuary at the top of the stairs in the house on 39th Street, but I didn't dare go out the door. It had been barely a week since the sorrow circus played out on our front porch. While the hordes had dispersed, there were still a few reporters; they waited in unmarked cars ready to lob questions if I dared leave the house.

The only pilgrimage allowed that day was the one I made to my espresso machine, where it waited on the kitchen countertop. Coffee. The smell of that espresso might just save me. I tamped the Italian roast into the basket, cranked the handle into position, turned the knob and waited as the viscous black liquid filled my cup. I breathed in the aroma, anticipating that elixir on my tongue. I filled my little metal pitcher with milk and turned the nozzle to froth.

Above the whine of the steamer, a loud guttural rumble filled the house and vibrated the floors. The front windows rattled on the other side of the thick draperies. *What the hell? Garbage truck? Fire truck?* Setting the pitcher on the counter, I padded through the dining room towards the front door. I snuck a peek from behind the tablecloth, a bright light flashed my face, blinding me, and sent my heart thudding.

"Look! Look! There he is!" A chorus of voices rang out in the dim light of dawn accompanied by peals of laughter. Out on Knott Street, a sleek black tour bus idled in front of the house. It had snapped a branch from the Japanese maple in our park strip, that branch now dangling like a broken arm from the top of the bus, pointed to the logo of a local radio station and a big banner plastered on its side that read: BRIDGETOWN'S TOUR OF SHAME. In the dim light, I could just make out another sign planted in the lawn between the Cedar tree and our front porch. In bold caps, it read "MALLORY'S BOY TOY." A crowd of people stood in line up our front walk in the dark morning, waiting their turn to have their picture taken next to the placard.

Furious, I ran to the back of the kitchen and picked up the phone to dial my uncle. "Mitch! There's a tour bus parked in front of our house. A sign on the lawn! People taking pictures."

"Don't worry, I'll take care of it." Within an hour the lawyer had called the radio station and threatened a lawsuit. Cease and desist. Later that day, the station aired a public apology stating their prank had been in poor taste. The same day an article appeared in our local paper comparing us to another Portland couple, Tonya Harding, and her club-wielding boyfriend.

———

A week after the press conference, Molly returned home, and one morning I shuffled into her room to wake her for school and found her asleep on the floor. She had pulled all her covers, sheets, comforters, and countless stuffed animals off the bed and built a nest on the rug.

"Molly, why are you on the floor?" I asked, down on my knees, hand on her cheek to wake her.

"Mallory slept in this bed, Mom. It's creepy." Mallory had given Molly the box spring and mattress before she left Portland for Washington D.C., she'd delivered it complete with a new set of Laura Ashley sheets.

"I can't take it with me." she'd said. Another gift to add to the pile, I'd thought then. My poor children, I think now.

I was unable to shield my daughter from the news. Mallory's face was everywhere, and Molly suffered a personal connection—her favorite babysitter, turned infamous celebrity combined with Charlie's involvement. Heartbreaking. Kids at school, perhaps courtesy of their parents, knew this and teased her. Articles appeared in newspapers across the country instructing parents on how to talk to their children about marital infidelity and oral sex.

"I bought Molly a new bed today," I announced to Charlie that night at dinner.

"What's wrong with the one she's got?" He shot me a glare.

"It creeps her out, Charlie."

"We don't have money for a new bed, Kate!"

"I charged it! Besides, I've got a plan, thought I'd drag the old one out to the sidewalk and hang a sign on it—MALLORY SLEPT HERE, MAKE OFFER."

"Not funny." Charlie glowered, stifling a grin.

———

Charlie took everything in stride and headed back to work as if nothing had happened. In the days leading up to our press conference, the media had swamped his workplace as well. By now, everyone—colleagues and the entire student body—were well acquainted with his wrongdoing, and the press had finally vacated the high school campus where he worked.

His first day back at work he was expected to run the lights for a school concert. He wanted his family at his side, solidarity he said. My reason for agreeing to go—reconnaissance.

The kids and I found seats at the back of the packed auditorium. The school principal was standing on the stage behind a microphone, and when she saw Charlie in the wings, she waved at him. "Let's welcome Charlie back, shall we?" Her voice boomed through the sound system. "Come on out here, Charlie," she motioned at him to take the stage. Loud cheers broke out as the entire audience jumped to their feet to applaud him with a standing ovation. I gasped. *An ovation for what?* I muttered to myself. *Sleeping with a former student? Or for his supporting role in a presidential sex scandal?*

"Thanks everyone, your support means the world to me." Charlie beamed from behind the microphone over claps and cheers. As soon as he slipped backstage to perform his duties, I tucked the kids in to their seats, surrounded by Charlie's students and colleagues, and instructed Molly to watch her brother.

I rushed from the auditorium down the hall to Charlie's office. Earlier that week, I'd found a letter from his co-worker tucked under the windshield wiper of the Suburban. From what she'd penned it was clear she did not think they were over. Furious, I had burned it in my fire bowl in the backyard. Tonight, I would search for more evidence, more fuel.

I opened the door to his office and there on his desk, the glint of a silver picture frame reflected the light from the hall. I switched on the desk lamp expecting to see a picture of Finn and Molly. Me? There on his desk, was a framed photograph of my husband with Cheryl, both dressed in their costumes as Uncle Henry and Auntie Em. Enraged, I rifled through his desk drawers and found a treasure trove of Mallory. Gifts she'd sent to his workplace—a different flavor—not the innocent decoy presents she sent to our home. Cards and notes with sexy messages, all of it covered in little strips of paper like trashy confetti, handwritten with racy notes describing all the things she'd like to do to him when next they met, and there at the bottom of that drawer was a necktie. I shoved all those nasty tidbits into my bag and flew in a blaze back to the auditorium, I slipped in next to Finn and made plans for my next driveway bonfire.

As we drove home, I said nothing about my discoveries.

Charlie went on about how wonderful it was to be welcomed back to work so warmly and with a standing ovation, no less.

"Disgusting," I said. "What, you're a hero for cheating on your wife?"

"Hero for telling the truth."

"Face it, Charlie. The only reason you told the truth is because you got caught."

44

THE DEAD CROW

Promises, promises, I'm all through with promises...
—Dionne Warwick

On the day the dead crow showed up at the end of my driveway, I knew exactly what to do with it. Tar black feathers, shiny in the morning sun, little black feet saluting the sky. I scooped the lifeless bird up with the blade of my shovel, carted it into our back garden and set it gently in the rain-flattened grass.

As luck would have it, Bob-the-Shaman was on his way over, and dead animals were definitely his department. I'd added the shaman to my staff of specialty caregivers at the urging of the lady that ran the local flower-essence pharmacy down the street. I paid him in custom-made pillows.

Bob-the-Shaman was a big old bear of a man. He reminded me of Kenny Rogers, though he wore his long, grizzled gray hair ponytailed with a leather lace. He came to my house once a week, on Wednesdays. I'd light a fire in the fireplace and lie on the living room floor. He'd chant a bit and balance my chakras, and then he'd move my energy around.

"Today we're going to work on your heart chakra." Bob-the-Shaman said, as I stretched out on the floor in front of the fire. His hands hovered like doves over my chest where my heart limped. "Blocked," he said.

"Broken," I said. *Shattered,* I thought, *like my plates.* It went on like this. My heart chakra was unresponsive and apparently slammed shut.

"We'll need to revisit this next week," Bob-the-Shaman said, as our session ended.

As soon as he got up off the floor, I walked him out back to show him the dead crow where I'd left it earlier that morning. "Whadya think?" I pointed to the bird.

"No visible signs of injury," he rolled the dead bird over gently, with the toe of his boot. "Looks like he may have died of old age."

"Really?" I knew better. After all, it was the third dead animal in two weeks. Last week I'd found a supine rat, stiff on the doorstep, a few days before it was a tiny chickadee in a shoebox. Nope, more likely, one of my husband's disgruntled lovers left it there overnight.

No matter. I knew the dead crow was a gift and just what I needed for my ritual that day.

"You should bury that crow," Bob-the-Shaman said as he left.

"Oh, I've got a plan." I walked Bob-the-Shaman out, twisting that promise ring around my chaffed finger.

The promise ring is what Charlie had called it; back on the day he'd come home loaded with gifts, a repentant sinner with meager offerings. With all that had happened in the last few weeks, just wearing it made me feel cheap, and with the discovery of the framed photo of one lover on his desk, coupled with the drawer full of tawdry gifts from the other, I was done with his promises.

I chose a spot along the fence where the crocuses were just beginning to pop their heads out of bed after the long, wet winter, I cracked the soft earth open with the blade of my shovel and I dug a shallow grave. I pulled that flimsy promise off my finger, threw it into the hole, and covered it with the lifeless crow. I shoveled the soil to cover them both, and then I said three prayers. One for the crow, and one for my children and one for the grace to live through this.

Back in the kitchen, I stood at the sink and washed the earth from my hands, massaging the red welt on my finger. Tears again. At any moment, with little or no warning, they made their trek down my cheeks. Who knew my eyes housed such a reservoir? I cleaned myself up, added WATERPROOF MASCARA to my shopping list, and headed out the door.

I used to enjoy my trips to Fred Meyer, Portland's local grocery store. Three football fields of teeming retail, everything from books to bath towels, car parts to cooking oil. An impossible land of distractions awaited me there. Back when my business was my business, before my heartbreak went public, it proved a handy escape. Errant husband home with the kids, I could claim a missing ingredient—a need to stock the larder—and spend time thumbing magazines or trying on tacky clothes. Now, in my current set of circumstances, it was more an obstacle course that could at any moment trigger the waterfall housed in my head. Still, I had to brave it. The kids would be home from school in two hours, and I had to get something for dinner.

Two days ago, it was the woman in the produce section. Slender, glossy dark hair, well dressed, the spike heels a give-away. She cornered me in front of a pyramid of shiny red deli-cious apples and touched my arm. "I'm so sorry, I'm praying for you. I wonder if I could ask you a few questions..."

On this day it was the guy in the bright blue Columbia Sportswear parka; the same guy I'd dodged at the edge of the soccer field the day before. Good looking—suspicious shopper —no basket, no cart. As he made his way toward me, I grabbed a couple bunches of fresh basil, glanced at my list, and fled produce for cosmetics. I searched the aisle for Maybelline. Scanning the assorted pink and green, I grabbed for the word WATERPROOF and tossed the mascara into my basket. Parka guy in pursuit.

I made a run for it pushing my cart, that damn clacking wheel making a racket out ahead of me. A quick detour and I was knee deep in party central, a colorful canyon festooned with wrapping paper and ribbons. I dashed past the greeting cards, made a quick jog and found myself surrounded by party favors. That's when I saw him, my childhood friend, Groucho Marx. I grabbed for those glasses, that honking nose and feathery black mustache, all wrapped in cellophane. Parka guy now right behind me, I ripped the package open, donned my disguise and turned to greet my pursuer. Imaginary cigar waggling at the corner of my mouth with the best Groucho I could conjure, "Hello, Sir, may I help you?"

Parka guy laughed out loud. "I'm so sorry, it's my job. I'd just like to ask you a few questions about your husband..."

"No comment."

I grabbed a few more Grouchos; threw them in the cart and beelined to the checkout stand still wearing my new disguise. The clerk laughed as I handed her my club card. I reached for a pack of Juicy Fruit, and that's when I saw them wedged between *Oprah* and *Sunset*, staring at me from the cover of the latest supermarket tabloid.

My husband's mistress, and her latest married man—the President of the United States of America.

45

MEN IN BLACK

In the weeks that followed, my uncle fielded calls from the media and phoned from LA every day to relay requests for interviews. He never suggested I do them, wanting only to keep me informed. The lawyer who acted as our spokesperson, had been contacted by the Starr Commission. They wanted to talk to us. A date was set. We would meet with the federal prosecutors leading the charge for the president's impeachment in the coming days. Until then, I followed the lawyer's instructions and gathered everything Mallory had sent to us from Washington, D.C.

The short drive from our house on Knott Street to our bank on 43rd turned caravan as suspicious cars with curious drivers followed close behind. I drove slowly on purpose. This cat and mouse game was getting old.

I'd called ahead and Ava, my personal banker, met me at the door. Her thick black hair curtained her face, black-brown eyes studded with concern. She glanced over my shoulder at a guy in a blue parka who'd followed me up the steps, now busying himself filling out a fake deposit slip. She whisked me into the back, through the gates, past the vault, into the room that housed the safety deposit boxes. No prying eyes here.

"I saw you on TV. Geez, Kate. You poor thing."

I unzipped the bulging duffle bag.

"Looks like you'll have to go big." She slid an extra-large box from its slot. In addition to the White House memorabilia that Mallory had sent us, I'd included all the cards, notes and photos she had given us over the years; all those I could find at the time, that is. Years later, I will purge the house. Twenty-plus years after the event, I still find stuff. Like fallout from a nuclear blast, remnants of her had sifted into every nook and cranny. Only last month, I found a birthday card she'd sent to me before I even knew her, with a note saying, "You don't know me yet, but Charlie mentioned your birthday, and I wanted to send you, my best." I thought it was weird at the time but had chalked it up to a friendly gesture.

Hand-me-downs she'd given to me, her lover's wife—jackets, shirts, coats, even a black nighty, perhaps embedded with my husband's DNA? Clothes I never wore. Fast forward, and in a few years, wanting it out of my house and strapped for cash, I will sell it all to a presidential memorabilia dealer on the east coast, expecting to make a discreet sale in exchange for a reduced price, but a handful of years later, he will make a big show of auctioning it all off. He'll want to buy her bed as well. Instead, I will drive her mattress to the dump and tip it over the edge, watching it plummet off the ledge of that cavernous garbage pit and bounce into an unsavory pile of smelly refuse.

———

My uncle returned to Portland ahead of our meeting with the officers from the Starr Commission to shepherd us through.

Word was out Starr's men were in town, and a slew of reporters had been staked out on Knott Street since dawn.

Mitch called to let me know he was on his way over, "It's me," he called through the door, letting me know it was safe to open. "Let's go shopping!" he grinned. "You'll need something to wear."

A Town Car, long, lean, and black, idled in the drive. "Don't make eye contact," he instructed. "I'll deal with those guys." Out the door, he ushered me into the back seat.

My uncle faced the parked cars, waved at the drivers with a smile, then climbed into the back seat next to me. "Let's have some fun!" A kid at heart, that grin and a playful twinkle in those deep-sea eyes, my uncle instructed our driver, "Drive us to the Federal Building! And go the long way around. Let's give 'em a run for their money." He turned to me with a chuckle.

Our driver, as instructed, led a bob and weave in and out of traffic. A chase ensued. A rat-tail of cars collected as our journey progressed across the river from the east side of Portland downtown to 3rd Street. "Pull up in front, right here," my uncle instructed. The driver slowed to a stop in front of the Federal Building. Mitch hopped out and held the door open for me, motioning with his hand to exit the car, but whispering, "Stay put." A long line of cars stacked up behind us and clogged the intersection. Cross traffic stood still, drivers honking. Mitch waved at the string of vehicles behind us and jumped back into the car, laughing.

"That was fun," our driver chuckled. "Where to next?"

"To the mall; my niece needs a new outfit." The driver dropped us at Pioneer Place. We dashed through the mall toward Talbots. Men in parkas tailed us as we entered the store. They hid behind racks of shirts and dresses, pants, and jackets. Amused salesclerks assisted as my uncle pulled possible options from the racks. He selected a blazer and a nice pair of slacks and sent me to the dressing room while the reporters hovered. My uncle fielded questions, lobbing "no comments" while I hid out in the dressing room, trying on clothes. It had been so long since I'd bought anything new and, despite losing twenty-five pounds, I still felt fat. Once fat, always fat. The body changes, but the brain is forever stuck with those extra pounds.

———

The next day, the same car and driver arrived to ferry us to the Riverfront Hotel downtown to meet with Kenneth Starr's investigators. When we arrived at the hotel, it was raining. The men met us out front with giant black umbrellas, and escorted us into separate hotel rooms, in the same corridor. Charlie in one room. Me in the other. They spoke to Charlie first. These men all here in Portland to take our statements and gather evidence. Evidence they hoped to find useful in their quest to impeach an American president.

For what felt like hours, I paced the room under the watchful eye of one of the officers, dressed in black, the squiggle of a plastic earpiece just visible above his collar. Uncomfortable in my new clothes, I waited my turn. I watched out the window to the Willamette River below, swollen and angry from the latest torrential downpour. Earlier that morning, as we dressed for this crazy thing we faced, Charlie chose a sport coat and tie. The irony nearly choked me. The only neckties he owned were all gifts from Mallory. Feeling the sting in this, I'd suggested he go tieless. He shook his head no. And I watched as he knotted Mallory's tie—a noose, around his neck.

Half an hour later three men entered the room. They looked like something out of a bad spy movie. All ill-fitting black suits, dark glasses. Wired, they asked their questions.

Nervous, I told them what I knew: the tie, the cards, the calls, the enchilada recipe. I detailed Mallory's ability to lie and deceive, as evidenced by her pretense of "friendship" while she bedded my husband. I told them this, certain that what I had to tell them paled in comparison to Charlie's sordid tales.

46

GROUCHO IN THE GLOVE BOX

"**M**omma! Someone's at the door!" Molly's voice rang through the house and found me where I stood in front of the kitchen sink, white-knuckled, with a mass of knots in my shoulders to match the ones in my head. The rain pelted the window and drummed my brain.

It had been weeks since our stupid circus act—the press conference on the front porch. Offers of big money poured in daily. *Inside Edition, Extra, Hard Copy*. I said no to all. It's not that I didn't need the money, I did, but I couldn't—make that wouldn't—expose my kids to any more of this.

Today the ladies from *Lifetime TV* called again. They'd upped the ante, offering six figures. I'd said no. Again. These ladies wanted to make a movie-of-the-week out of me. The story they were pitching wasn't my story; it was the story they wanted to tell; the story they knew would sell. Besides, how I got here and how I would get out, was still being written. I didn't know my ending yet.

"Mom!" I trudged the diagonal path from the kitchen to the entryway. Molly and Finn were parked on the sofa, the backs of their heads—two half-moons just visible over the mountain of couch. They sang along with Dumbo in the darkened room. *"Look out for Mr. Stork, he'll find you in the end."* Damn. That. Stork.

Our hardwoods hadn't seen the light of day for weeks now. The drapes I'd sewn to dress our home, were still drawn tight like battle lines. The top half of our front door was still covered as well.

A knock at the door—it could be anything. Forgoing my usual precautions, I forgot to peek and opened the door. Big mistake.

There she was, my nemesis, the pesky neighborhood stringer. Her freckles scattered across her face like buckshot, unkempt curly red-brown hair frazzled around her head in the driving wind and rain. That sad old army surplus jacket, the one she always wore, more drab and depressing than ever. How lucky was I, this "journalist" lived down the street, just three blocks away? Her kid was on Molly's soccer team. I had to dodge her in the halls at school.

Today, no dodge—fully frontal, she stood on my front porch holding the latest edition of the *National Enquirer* like a banner in her hand. She waved that sorry rag in my face. The president and his mistress—their faces flagging in the wind.

"Just a few questions?"

"Are you kidding me? How many times do I have to ask? Leave us alone! Stay away from me and my kids and take that piece of crap with you!" I slammed the door in her face. Third time that month.

The kids jumped in their skin. "Mom! Language!" they chorused as I raced through the house. *FuckFuckFuck!!!* I flew out the back door into the wind and the rain and ran toward relief, just a few yards away.

Did I mention that I break things?

Sometimes rage, sometimes sorrow, on any given day, when the urge overtook me, I made the short pilgrimage across the yard to the little garden outside my workshop. I'm sure if you listened very carefully, you'd hear those weathered clapboards cry, "Brace yourselves, lads! Here she comes!"

I kept plates and bowls stacked at the ready just on the other side of the weathered picket fence for situations just like this one. I would fling cups and saucers, dinner and dessert plates at the side of the garage with all my might. Shards would splinter and fly and find a new home in the fertile soil of my little vegetable garden. All these years later, I know that something in that shattering released me bit by bit. But damn! No release today. *FuckFuckFuck!* I ran back into the house, dripped through the door. Tracked mud on the floor. That damn white floor.

"Kids, get your coats."

"Where are we going?"

"We need more dishes!"

"Yay!" they sang. They knew the drill.

We stood inside the door, all three bundled against the wind and the rain. "Ready?" I stepped out to check. "All clear!" I called. "Let's go!"

We were out on the porch, ready to run, but before I could shut the door, Finn stopped short. He made a quick U-turn, toddled back inside, pulled his Bubba from its perch on his shoulder and ever so gently set his beloved companion down on the entry floor just inside the door.

"Finn-honey, get your Bubba."

"Finn, get Bubba," Molly parroted, her eyes wide with surprise. We never left home without Bubba. Ever. Entire outings had been stalled or canceled if Bubba was misplaced or mistakenly left behind.

"Get Bubba," Molly repeated.

"Nope." He shook his head with defiance. "Bubba's gotta stay home," he declared. "Bubba's gonna gawd the house fwom weporters!"

My heart broke in a hundred ways. A plate flew at the cage of my ribs and shattered in my chest. My little boy knew we needed protection and that his Bubba, furless and flattened, was the best man for the job.

I caught the sob that threatened my throat, picked Finn up and breathed him in. "Thank you, sweet boy." A tear escaped, trailed down my cheek. I pulled the door closed, locked it tight, looked left then right, and we ran through the rain to our car in the drive. I loaded Finn into his car seat.

"You sure about Bubba?" Molly asked again while buckling him in.

"I'm sewre."

I climbed into the driver's seat. Locked the doors and gripped the wheel.

"Ready?" I asked my trusty passengers.

"Groucho!" They chimed.

"Right, Groucho!" I leaned across the passenger seat and pulled three pairs of Groucho Marx glasses out of the glove box. I'd kept them there since the day I was chased through Fred's by that suspicious non-shopper who'd begged me for an interview. We wore them now when we went out in public. Six blue eyes rimmed with black plastic glasses, feathered eyebrows, and furry mustaches—three little noses hidden behind that giant plastic proboscis. We donned our disguises. People pointed and laughed. And maybe, just maybe, they laughed because we wanted them to, because we looked silly, and not because we were the local sideshow in a national scandal.

It was a short drive from our house on Knott Street to the Goodwill on Broadway. Once inside, Finn loaded in the cart,

Molly pushing, I led the way. We cruised past the vast array of discarded personal belongings. The odor of old clothes and the old men who wore them staled the air. We passed coats way past their prime and endless racks of flannel shirts in various degrees of fade. We were on a mission, we three, behind our glasses and mustaches. We hightailed it to housewares, and there they were, stacks of dishes just waiting to sacrifice themselves in the name of my mental health. We scavenged those stacks. I let the kids select their own. We loaded the cart and wheeled our loot to the checkout.

"Whoa! Great glasses!" the checker said with a chuckle. She rang us up and lo and behold, it was our lucky day. Housewares Wednesday! All dishes half off! See? I told the kids—and myself, "Blessings abound." I said a silent prayer of thanks to Mary, and then we three Grouchos headed out the door. I loaded the trunk. People pointed and laughed. The kids and I giggled and headed towards home. All will be well, I told myself. I'll figure this out.

And hey...we made it home without a tail. Groucho's back in the glove box. We've got dishes for days.

And Bubba? Bubba was right back where he belonged, on my sweet Finny's shoulder.

47

DEAD IN MY HEART

Bob-the-Shaman taught me an ancient Native American ritual: "Dead in my heart." I chanted this sentence while thudding my heart chakra with my fist. Dead in my heart. Dead in my heart. Mary-Mary-Mary. I practiced this several times a day, determined that when Charlie was gone, I would not spend one moment pining for him. My job was to pull him out of my heart by the roots and take a stitch ripper to that knotted promise that seamed me to him. I did this all while we slept under the same roof in separate beds. A keen observer, I watched him now without the love-goggles on. Love-googles— those lying lenses that had caused me to see a beloved in a briar patch of a man. I watched detached, to see who he was, and who I was without him.

Worry still threaded my days, but there was also wonder. There were signs in everything, dash clocks, license plates, odometer readings. All had numerical messages for me. Books fell open to pages full of important passages. Rumi told me this: *"What I long for, you know will kill me; what I think will kill me, you know will heal me."* And I knew this: there was a gift in this devastation.

There was still rain, but now there was sun in that rain. There were rainbows everywhere, on the horizon, over my neighborhood. Sun danced through raindrops as they bounced off the hood of my car, refracting rainbows as I drove across the Burnside Bridge.

Complete strangers recognized me on the street, in the market, at the mall, and approached me with kindness, to say "I am praying for you." I thanked them and knew their prayers were working.

One day in therapy, I recounted the euphoria I'd experienced when my marriage to Hank finally ended. He went out the door and I locked it tight. Deadbolt. And chain. I checked on my baby girl—deliciously asleep and unaware and whispered, "It's just you and me, Molly, and we'll be fine."

Then I celebrated. Everything in that moment felt holy. I put Joni on low, and she sang to me. I was her free man in Paris —unfettered and alive. I lit candles. I burned incense. I knelt on the hearth and lit a fire, and took my first deep breath in over a year. No sorrow, just gratitude. And then, I had the distinct sensation of a rose unfurling in my heart.

That day, my therapist quoting Mary Oliver, asked, "Kate, what is it you plan to do with your one wild and precious life?" This question filled me with hope for a future I'd begun to imagine.

In time, I understood the vow I'd made was a vow that had been voided by Charlie's blatant disregard. To remain committed to this marriage was to pledge myself to a sham—a self-betrayal. I had released myself from Promise Prison and I would undo my "I do." My task now—to free myself with a plan to care for my children.

—————

I sat at my big pine table and faced a stack of bills. How would I pay these without Charlie's paycheck? The only hope as I saw it was Chairwear. I knew if I could grow my little business, and work from home, this would go further to support us than anything I could find in the want ads.

Just then, Jane, our babysitter, arrived for her afternoon shift in tears. I took her in my arms and held her tight. She'd had another fight with her mother. "She kicked me out of the house," she sobbed. Still in high school, this young girl wore no make-up and had bright copper-colored hair and freckled skin. A straight "A" student, so tender with my kids, she was more a big sister than babysitter to Molly and Finn. The battles between this mother and daughter were unfathomable from my vantage point. Heartbroken for her, her relationship with her mother, rife with battles and anger, was so like mine.

"Where will I go?" she blew her nose into a wad of tissues.

A light bulb flashed my brain. "How about room and board in exchange for babysitting?"

"Really?" Jane's eyes brightened.

Thank you, Mary. I eyed those bills. This arrangement meant I could save the cash I paid her each week and with her live-in help, I could grow my business.

It wouldn't be enough, but it was a start.

48

INSIDE ADDITION

The ladies at *Lifetime TV* had called again that morning. Still offering six figures through the phone lines, they'd sent videotapes of tasteful TV movies they had done, hoping to convince me. "We want to tell your side of the story, a woman's story," they said.

I said no. Again. We'd been through enough, I reasoned, and I did not want to expose my kids to any more of this. They would understand what their father had done at some point in the future, but I would not add to the lexicon. Larry Flint's people called asking for anything on Mallory, a fortune paid for intimate details or artifacts. No, definitely not. But in the meantime, I beseeched Mary daily for guidance, for help, for a clear sign. A ticket out.

That afternoon the women from *Inside Edition* arrived on my front porch. They wore smart suits, narrow skirts, and matching jackets, they were trim and attractive, in a TV kind of way. My uncle had called to warn me they were coming. "This one, you should do," he'd said. He knew I needed money and felt of all the offers I'd received these women would be sympathetic.

I no longer recall how many stood there on my doorstep with briefcases and clipboards in hand when I opened the door. Four, maybe five. They arrived en masse, determined. I let them in. These ladies were practiced in their pumps. I sat them in the living room, cast in darkness, drapes still pulled tight. They'd been calling for weeks now, requesting an interview. They'd offered to fly me to Los Angeles, to put me up in a nice hotel. A vacation, they'd purred. I'd said no. So, they took to the air and brought their offer to me.

"We are prepared to pay you for this interview." The ring-leader spoke first, her coiffed hair, styled close to her head. "This is not something we normally do. We want your side of the story. What it's like to be a woman, a wife, a mother, caught in this maelstrom."

"My kids have been through so much already." I replied.

"Would you agree if we gave you control over the interview questions?"

So afraid they'd ask if I'd considered divorce during the interview, and not wanting to lie, the thought that I could pre-approve their questions did sweeten the deal. I'd told no one, save Marina, that I would not stay in my marriage. I would not alert the media of my intentions.

We went round and round until one of the women said, "At the very least, let us buy you a nice lunch."

"Okay," I said. "Lunch."

We piled into a big booth at a local steakhouse, Cobb salads and iced teas all around. Just ladies at lunch. The conversation turned from TV interviews to motherhood. Two or three of these women were new mothers, still nursing. We spoke of breast infections, the trials of teething and sleepless nights. This sorority of motherhood—a shared experience. They all expressed sincere sympathy at what I'd faced in my marriage; infidelity, compounded by the national media attention. As we chatted and compared notes, a familiar name bubbled to the surface. Three of these women had taken Lamaze classes in LA from my old friend, Jenny. A sign? Perhaps.

Our lunch ended, and they asked me to consider their offer. The money they offered was a modest sum compared to the six figures from *Lifetime TV*. But I did the math, and it would be just enough money to keep my kids and me in the house on Knott Street for one more year without any help from Charlie. We finished our lunch, and I promised to think about it. Once they had left and flown back to Los Angeles, I did some checking and discovered *Inside Edition* aired at midnight in Portland. This, back before the internet and the ability to stream content online. No one would see it, I reasoned.

———

Later that night, I lay sleepless in my bed at the top of the stairs and rolled to the clock. 3:33. I acknowledged that numerical message—three threes signified a decision had been made. And I decided. I would do the interview. I would take the money. And at long last, I would have the means to kick Charlie out of our house.

Next order of business: to pee.

I threw on my robe and padded down the stairs to the bathroom. The house was dark and quiet. I made my way through the dining room on tiptoe not wanting to wake anyone. I crossed the entry and turned towards the bath. There was movement on the couch. I flipped on the lamp that sat on the sofa table and there they were, a jumble of arms and legs, red hair and blond, my husband wrapped around Jane, our babysitter.

"Unbelievable!" I screamed at the top of my lungs.

Jane untangled herself from my husband and jumped to her feet, "Oh, Kate, I'm so sorry. Charlie is just so sad."

"We were only comforting each other!" my husband cried.

"Jane, tomorrow you will pack your bags and leave. Charlie, I'm done. I want you out of this house."

I turned and headed back up the stairs, Charlie following close behind me.

"Kate," he tailed me up the stairs, crying. "We weren't doing anything! We were just talking, we fell asleep."

"Charlie, I want you out of this house, I want you gone. We are done." Charlie fell to the floor in a heap at the top of the stairs and sobbed, he clutched my ankles with his hands. "Let go of me!" I screamed as he cried and begged, streams of mucus clotting in his hair.

"Please! Kate don't do this to us! Don't do this to me! Please! How can you ruin our family this way?"

"Ruin our family? Me? Did you really just say that?"

Then, there they were, those words Charlie had instructed me to use all those years ago when dealing with Hank. Out my mouth, they came, as if they'd lain in wait for that very moment.

"Suck my dick, Charlie. Just suck my big dick!"

49

THE MADONNA OF BROKEN DISHES

"**M**om, what's for dinner?" Molly called out from the living room to the kitchen, where I rummaged through the pantry for the Pepperidge Farm breadcrumbs.

"I'm thinking crummy chicken."

"Yay! Crummy chicken!" Finn and Molly echoed back.

I peeled the blue plastic lid back from the paper cylinder, nearly empty. *Damn!*

"Come on, kids, we have to run to the store."

"Mom!" Molly, all ten-year-old exasperation pleaded, "I'm old enough to babysit." True, it would take me ten, twelve minutes round-trip tops and it had been months since anyone had shown up at our door, though I still kept all the doors and windows covered.

"Okay," I said, "but do not answer the door."

Fifteen minutes later, barely through the door, Finn tackled my knees. "Momma! A weporter!" He stared up at me, arms tight around my legs.

I looked to Molly, her brow furrowed with worry. "Mommy, I'm sorry. I made a mistake."

"What is it, Honey?"

"A reporter came to the door right after you left. She wanted to talk to Charlie." Molly handed me a business card emblazoned with the NBC peacock.

"What did you say?"

"I told her he doesn't live here anymore."

It had been five months since I'd kicked Charlie out of the house, and I had managed to keep our separation from the press. I'd done the *Inside Edition* interview, giving no indication that I planned to end my marriage. I could see it all coming at me in a fiery news flash, another slew of reporters on my doorstep, my private decision to divorce, now fodder for the pages of the *National Enquirer*.

I sprinted to the kitchen, set my grocery bag down on the counter, picked up the phone, and called my uncle. Within ten minutes we'd crafted a press release announcing my decision to end my marriage—a preemptive strike. I would control this narrative. The press would not victimize me. Not again.

"I'll take care of getting this out," said my uncle.

Then, out the back door, I flew in the direction of my fallow vegetable garden. A few surviving plates waited in the stack by the gate. It had been a few months since the urge to smash dishes had forced me out to my killing field. But this invasion of my privacy, this coerced confession, enraged me.

I reached for the plate on top of the stack, cocked my arm, prepared to send another dish to its death, but before I released it, before I let it fly, a tiny glint of light caught my eye. The endless rain of the day had ceased, and for a moment sunlight bathed the yard. That glint, a little beam of light in the hedge, forced me to set my intended projectile down and investigate. I trudged through the muddy earth, spiked with pottery shards, and there in the privet hedge at the back edge of my garden, held upright in a delicate web of twigs, was a rose-covered teacup. A cup I'd intended to smash had somehow survived my fury and had lodged there over winter into spring. A fragile vessel brimming with raindrops and tiny leaves—a sacred tea. Whole and unbroken.

———

The yard art Madonna with her chipped and flaking paint, so holy when I spied her through the darkened shop window of the vintage store next to the laundromat. She called to me. The soft glow of a nightlight haloed her where she stood amidst the fiesta-ware bowls and old frames holding a collection of paint-by-number masterpieces. That night, I dreamt of her and the next day, I headed back to the shop to see her. I wanted her. The hundred-dollar price tag was a hundred dollars I did not have, or at least, should not spend on a concrete statue of Mary. Besides, where would I put her? I'd never been one for yard art, and my neighbors would definitely not approve. There were no garden trolls, gnomes, or concrete deer in these yards.

Still, she haunted me. Her peeling white paint, like lace-work, the blue-green orb she stood on, many-layered shades of turquoise faceted the fissured surface. Someone had loved her, this painted lady, as I did now. Perhaps I could put her in the back garden atop the burial site of the crow and that ring? No. And still, I obsessed. I reasoned and bargained. I wanted her in my home.

The next day, there was a faint knock at the door, and I had a thought to ignore it. I braved a peek. It was my landlady, Marion, I opened the door to let her in.

"Hello, Kate. I need to talk to you. Can we sit down?" I ushered her in and she took a seat in the living room.

"What is it, Marion?" My stomach a fist of worry.

"Honey, I'm so sorry. After all you've been through in the last year, I hate to do this, but I need to sell the house."

I took an airless breath. "Move out? Marion, it's the middle of the school year. What about the kids? My business? When?"

"End of February."

"One month? You want me to pack and move in one month?"

"March at the latest," she apologized again and stood to leave.

Shell-shocked, I let her out the door, headed to the kitchen and lifted the phone to dial Marina.

"Hey, girl! I was just gonna call you!" Marina's voice, a husky chuckle in my ear.

"Oh Marina, Marion's kicking me out of the house. She needs to sell it."

"Look, I've always known I bought the house on 39th for you," she chimed, without hesitation. We discussed the rent and settled on an amount I thought I could afford. "But here's the thing," she added. "The home inspector said a fire in that fireplace would burn the house to the ground. You can never build a fire. Promise me."

"I promise." And then in a flash, I knew where Mary belonged. That peeling Madonna, my Mother Mary, would stand at the end of that long front room on the tiled hearth in front of Marina's non-working fireplace.

———

Months later, on a warm spring day, all settled in our new home, I heard the hollow sound of footsteps on the wooden front porch and a familiar voice calling through the screen door.

I walked from the kitchen to find my old landlady, standing

on the other side of the screen, the Daphne I'd planted on either side of the front steps was filling the air with perfume. "Hello, Marion. What brings you here?"

"I brought you a gift," she said, a gentle smile on her lips. I unlatched the hook on the old screen door; the squeaky creak of its hinges welcomed her in.

In her hands, she held a large white box tied with a pink satin ribbon. She handed it to me. "What is it? I asked as I lifted the box from her hands. It was heavy and the contents rattled as I set it down on the entry table.

"Open it. You'll see."

I loosened the ribbons, tugged the bow free, and lifted the top off the box as an earthy fragrance wafted free.

"I thought you might want these," she said. "I collected them for you."

There in the box, caked with earth—were all the broken pieces of me. She'd filled that box to the brim with shards of broken plates and cups and saucers. All my rage and sorrow contained in that box. Years of heartbreak and betrayal done up in a bow.

"Thank you, Marion," I said as she turned to leave.

I held that box, heavy in my hands, surveyed all those broken bits, and knew I had done it, I had welcomed and entertained every sorrow, anger, rage, each and every shattered bit, just as Rumi had instructed.

I tied those pink ribbons back into a bow and walked the box the length of the room. I knelt before my Mary and laid the box at her feet. Tears of gratitude trailed my cheeks. And there on my knees, I said a prayer of thanks. No sorrow, just gratitude.

And my heart opened like a rose.

EPILOGUE

Start walking...your legs will get heavy and tired.
Then comes a moment of feeling the wings you've grown, lifting.
—Rumi

The ritual Bob-the-Shaman taught me had worked; Charlie was indeed dead in my heart. By the time I'd booted him out, there was no trace of pining. I was truly done. In the months following his departure, my depression lifted, and I grew stronger. The kids and I made fewer trips to Goodwill for dishes, as the anger requiring their sacrifice subsided. At some point, we even retired our Groucho glasses.

As a result of my self-authored press release, *Time Magazine* listed my decision to divorce Charlie in their Milestones column. I laughed out loud when I saw it, right there under the announcement of Popeye's engagement to Olive Oyl. *Perfect*, I'd thought. Triumphant, I took heart—rather than being used by the press, I had used them to declare my freedom.

A deep sense of well-being surfaced as I learned to trust my gut. I listened carefully. Gradually, I restored myself and gained a sense of self—rooted in myself—not in another.

As a kid, when I imagined my adult life, I pictured this: me —two kids—no man. Always. To this day, I wonder, was this prescience? Preordained? Or had I created it by imagining it? At the age of eighteen, I'd made three pronouncements: One, I would never marry. Two, I would never own a Volvo station wagon. And three, I would never ever drive a minivan. I'd only managed to hold the line at the minivan.

What makes us know ourselves and then forget?

As a girl born in the late 1950s, marriage was expected of me. Case in point: My mother did not give me a middle name. Her reason? I would marry and use my maiden name as my middle name. The message: I was incomplete without a HIM. Was it the pressure of paradigm—the societal messages that told me I was incomplete without my "other-half?" In my case, it was the gnawing sense that without marriage there was something missing. In the end, I believed true happiness resided in the promise of marriage, a promise of partnership.

Turns out, I could not choose a suitable partner until I learned to partner myself.

Certain I was better off alone, I did not date. I courted myself. I chose to stay in Portland and raise my kids surrounded by dear friends. I cooked good meals and read bedtime stories and built my business.

Chairwear thrived. It turned out making new clothes for old furniture combined with the flexibility of being my own boss, made single motherhood a dream. Eventually, I moved the business out of the house into a shop in a charming turn-of-the-century building consisting of five small storefronts, a quick five-minute drive from the house on 39th street. The day I signed the lease, I was nervous. But in my heart, my gut, I knew this commitment was a good one.

No fixed hours, I could leave the shop whenever I wanted, run errands, pick the kids up at school or shop for dinner. Yes, things were tight financially, some months were flush, others we barely made it. But we got by. Just my kids and me—no man. I'd never been happier.

Funny, in those days I only remember sunshine. My shop, at the east end of the building, benefited from a large bank of windows. Sun would stream through the glass, light my cutting table, and illuminate the fat rolls of velvets, silks, and cottons, stored beneath it—all waiting to be cut and whipped into a steady stream of slipcovers or Roman shades or draperies. This place was a sanctuary for me. The drafting of patterns, the heft of the shears in my hand as I cut the cloth, the steady hum of my industrial sewing machine, yards and yards of fabric guided by my hands under the *tick-tick-tick* of the speeding needle. This alchemy—this stitching of things together to create something beautiful and new, stitched me together too. A daily meditation. And always: Mary-Mary-Mary.

Ten years after I divorced Charlie, Finn in middle school, and Molly away at college, I arrived at my shop and stepped over the scatter of mail that had fallen through the door slot that morning. I knelt to collect it and tucked between grocery store circulars and utility bills, I found a pink envelope, the handwriting vaguely familiar. When I opened it and read the first few lines, my mind stalled. It was from Mallory.

Handwritten entirely in lower-case, she wished me well. She acknowledged her betrayal and then she apologized, adding that there were things she wished I hadn't said or done when everything went public, but that I was a good person who hadn't deserved what had happened. She concluded by asking for my forgiveness.

Hafiz says, *"Forgiveness is the cash we need."* I've always believed the act of forgiveness belongs to the gods. I've tried to cultivate a practice of acceptance and gratitude as I've searched for meaning in the things that befall me. I believe this practice has fostered something akin to forgiveness—and has indeed been the "cash" I needed to free myself and move forward.

We've all made choices we wish we hadn't. If we're lucky, our poor choices seed our growth and become the treasure we carry forward to create our best lives. This is my deepest wish for all of us.

Rumi told me, *"Be grateful for whoever comes because each has been sent as a guide from beyond."* I know every misfortune, every stone in my path, has contained a hidden gift that has caused me to examine my life and make better choices as I've charted my way forward. I have learned to trust my intuition, those whispered hints of long ago, now amplified, guide me daily. The pains I've experienced, though once certain they would kill me, have served to reroute me—a course correction— that has healed me and led the way to my right life. For this, I am grateful.

In the end, I know everything is perfect, even when it's not.

And the best part—Rumi kept his promise. My particular "crowd of sorrows," those unexpected visitors, were a gift and did precisely what he promised they'd do—they cleared me out for a new delight.

Quite simply, the life I'm living now.

ACKNOWLEDGMENTS

Rumi says, *"Sometimes a door opens, and a human being becomes a way for grace to come through."* Countless beings came to my aid while I lived this, and later when I knew I had to write it. To all the dear friends and beautiful humans who have been open doors and the source of so much grace. I am forever grateful.

Deepest gratitude to my agent, Lindsay Edgecombe, for seeing promise in my pages and taking me on. Endless thanks to my editor, Kerri Kolen, for your guidance and encouragement to go deeper. To Rachel Smalter-Hall and the team at Audible. And to Shaun Loftus, Rachel Curran, and the rest of the gang at Book Whisperer, *grazie mille* for all your help in getting my words on the page.

Thanks to my dear friends and earliest readers. To Lee Montgomery, who said, "write this one." To Anna Boorstin, who encouraged me to write the hard parts. To Whitney Otto and to Hope Edelman, who shared their insights and edits early on. To Marion Winik, for your advice and your humor. To Debra Winegarten, gone too soon. I feel you, my friend. To everyone at The Writer's Hotel. To the Community of Writers for inviting me in and to my fellow "Niners," with special thanks to Nichole LeFevbre, for your kind introduction to Lindsay. And to Mary Afsari, our friendship has been a life raft as we've written our way through to the end.

Eternal thanks to Rumi and to the friend who introduced

us all those years ago, knowing his words were the medicine I needed. Gratitude to his translators, Coleman Barks and Andrew Harvey, your inspired translations led me through.

Special thanks to the Knott Street Gang, Polly, Tori, James, and Robert, for your friendship; you stood by me when things got nutty. To "Marina" for the refuge on 39th and for the use of your closet. To Edwin, rest well dear friend, I miss you.

To my "three graces" Terry, Sally, and Kimi. You've seen it all. You are my touchstones and my treasures.

To Uncle Michael, for everything.

To my mother and father, who filled our home with books and fostered my devotion to the written word. And to my sisters, for being there.

To my children, you have anchored me while we surfed my learning curve. I thank you and I love you so. I pray your lives are filled with sweet slices of pie.

And to my beloved Tad, for your unyielding support. You are proof that two wrongs *do* make a right.

And always, Mary-Mary-Mary.

A NOTE TO READERS

Dear Reader,

Thanks so much for picking up a copy of *Everything Is Perfect*. Writers are nothing without their readers and I'd love to hear from you. You can get in touch via my website, www.katenason writes.com.

Warmest regards,
    Kate Nason

ABOUT THE AUTHOR

Kate Nason was born in Los Angeles, California, and earned her degree in art history at UCLA. After graduation she left LA for Florence, Italy, where she intended to live forever. Two jobless years later, she reluctantly returned to Los Angeles to enjoy a rewarding career in the LA art world. She did all of this while simultaneously making dreadful choices in men.

In the 90's, Kate moved with her young family to Portland, Oregon. There she divorced her second mistake, ran her own design business, and raised two children as a happily-single mother. Kate still lives in Portland. She returns to Florence every chance she gets. Everything Is Perfect is her debut memoir.

Made in United States
North Haven, CT
17 May 2023

36705924R00157